Pink Floyd • Guitar Tab Anthology

Si ringraziano tutti gli Editori coinvolti nel progetto.

ANOTHER BRICK IN THE WALL (Part 1) 6
ANOTHER BRICK IN THE WALL (Part 2) 16
ASTRONOMY DOMINE 22
BRAIN DAMAGE 29
BREATHE 50
COMFORTABLY NUMB 38
ECLIPSE 57
GOODBYE BLUE SKY 62
HAVE A CIGAR 67
HEY YOU 76
IF 86
IS THERE ANYBODY OUT THERE? 90
MONEY 93
MOTHER 122
NOT NOW JOHN 110
ON THE TURNING AWAY 116
REMEMBER A DAY 129
SEE EMILY PLAY 132
SHINE ON YOU CRAZY DIAMOND (PART V) 136
WELCOME TO THE MACHINE 148
WISH YOU WERE HERE 142

Legenda

ANOTHER BRICK IN THE WALL (Part 1)

Testo e Musica di Roger Waters

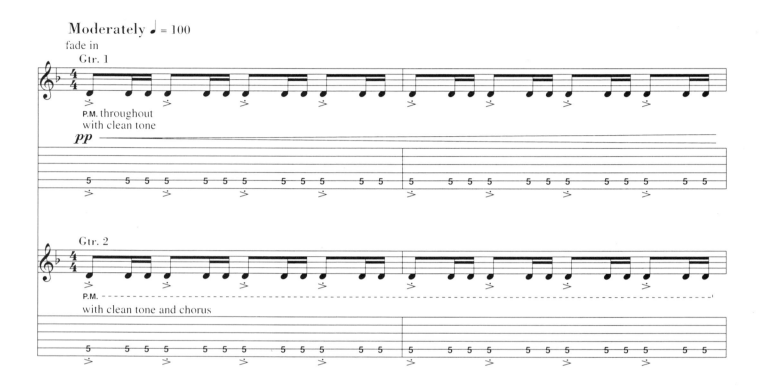

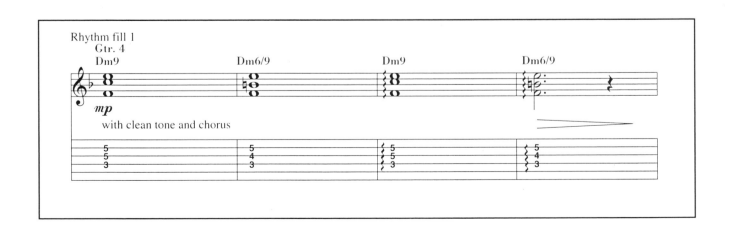

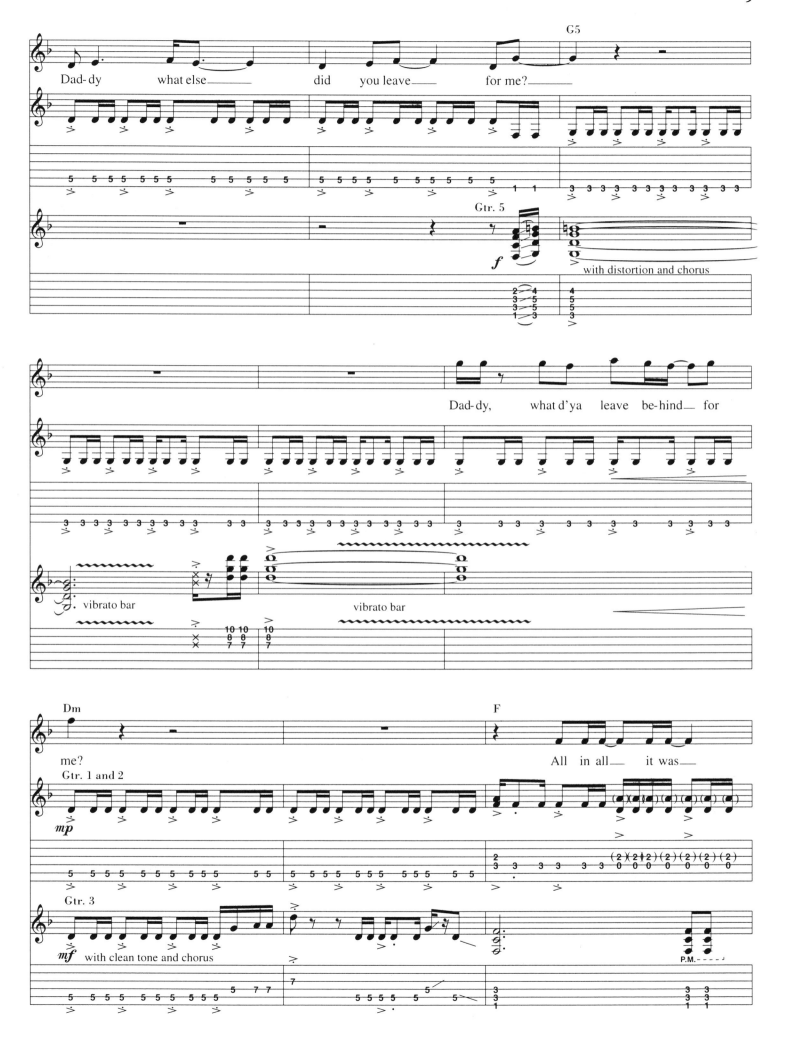

with schoolyard sound effects

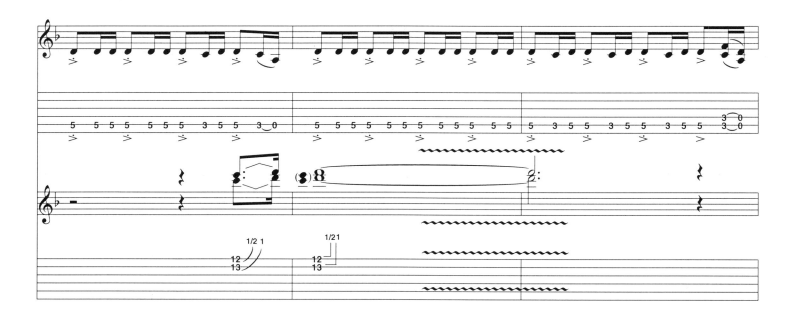

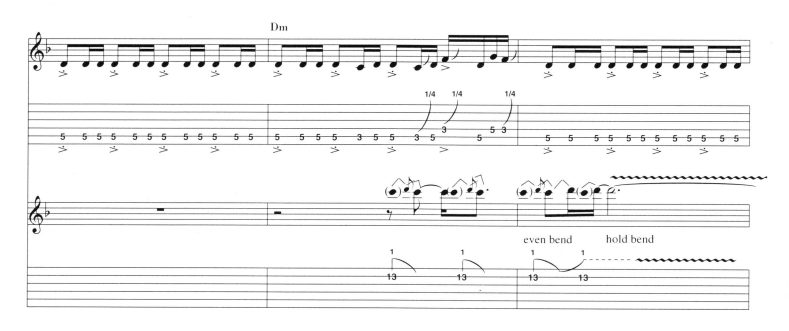

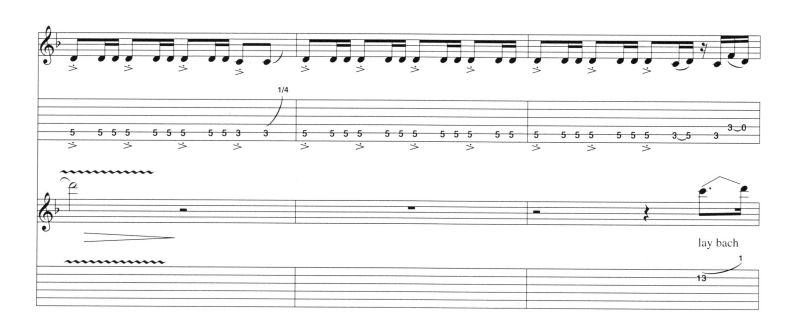

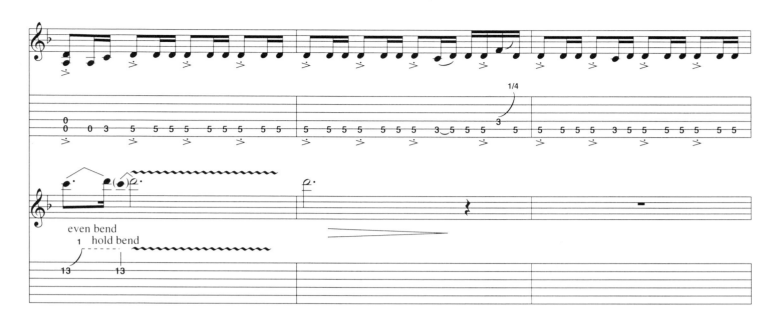

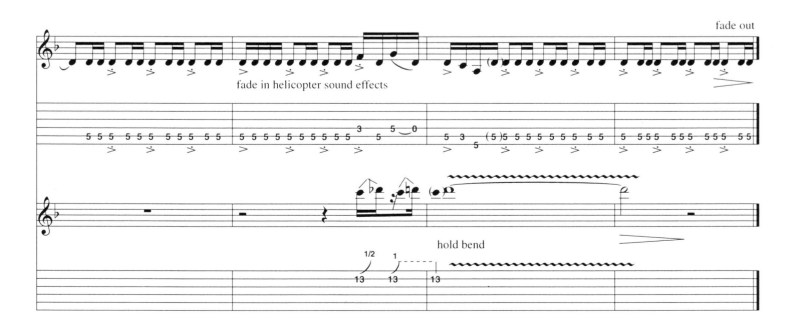

ANOTHER BRICK IN THE WALL (Part 2)

Testo e Musica di Roger Waters

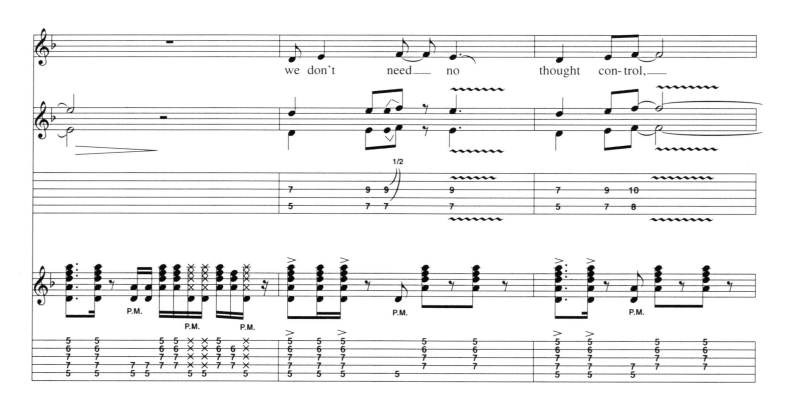

Teach - er leave____ them   kids   a-lone.____

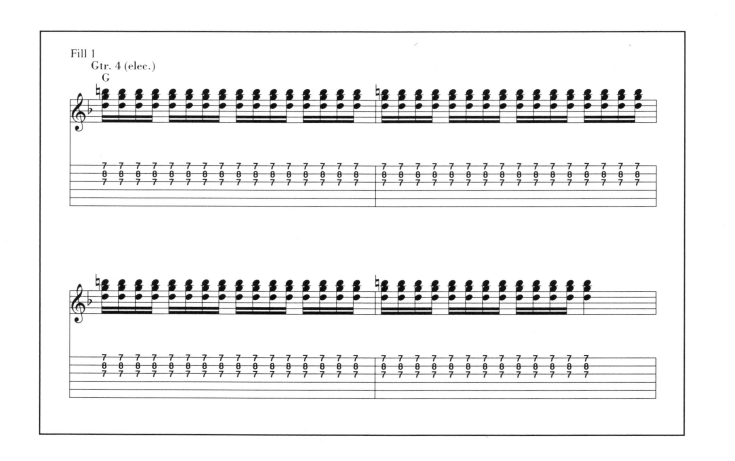

Fill 1
Gtr. 4 (elec.)

All in all_ it's just an - - - other brick in the_ wall.
All in all_ it's just an - - - other brick in the_

wall.

Gtr. (Solo)

slow release

rake   rake

ASTRONOMY DOMINE

Testo e Musica di Syd Barrett

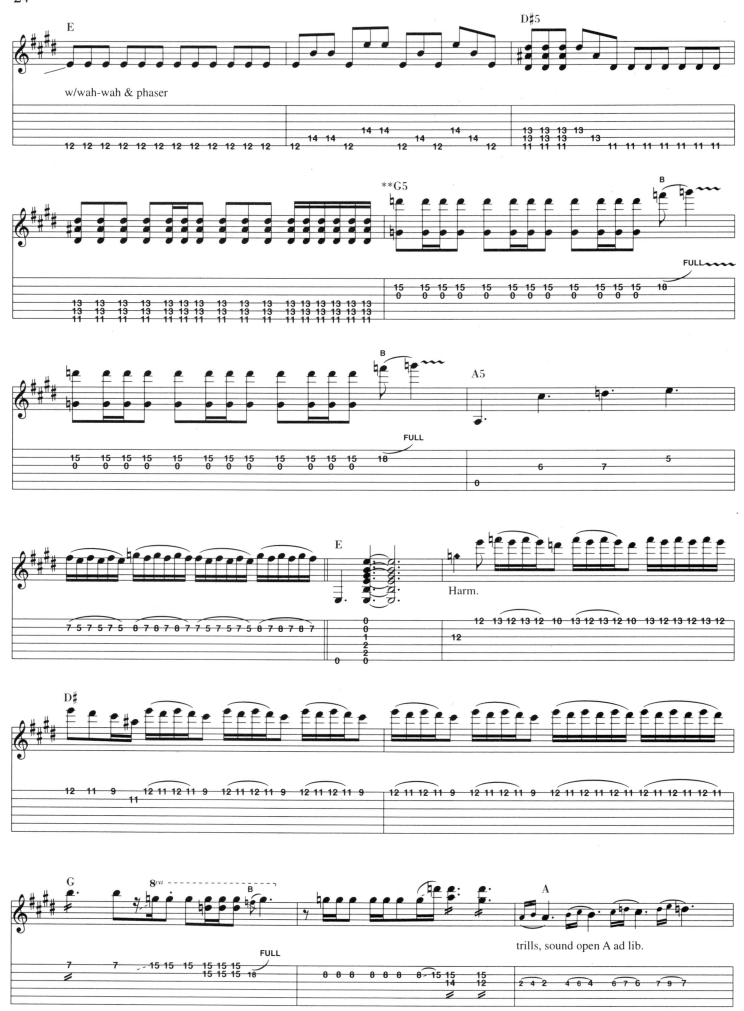

26

28

BRAIN DAMAGE

Testo e Musica di Roger Waters

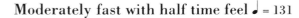

Moderately fast with half time feel ♩ = 131

Intro

The lu - na - tic —— is on the grass, ——

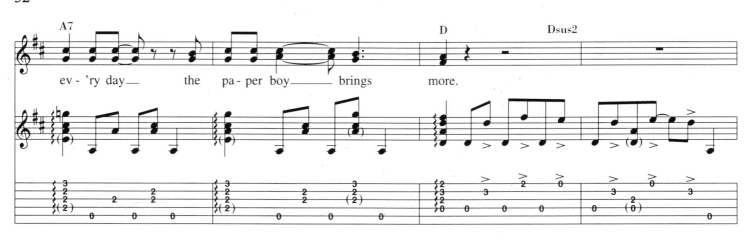

fore-bod - ings, too,___ I'll see you in the dark___ side___ of the moon.

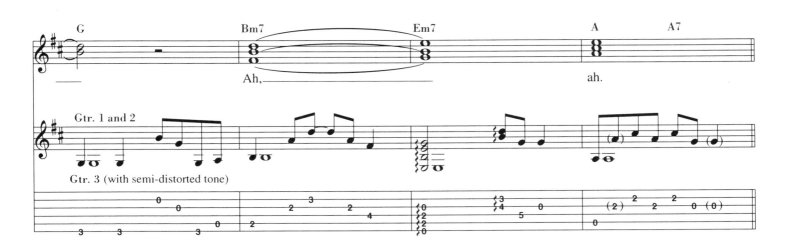

Gtr. 1 and 2

Gtr. 3 (with semi-distorted tone)

Ah,_____ ah.

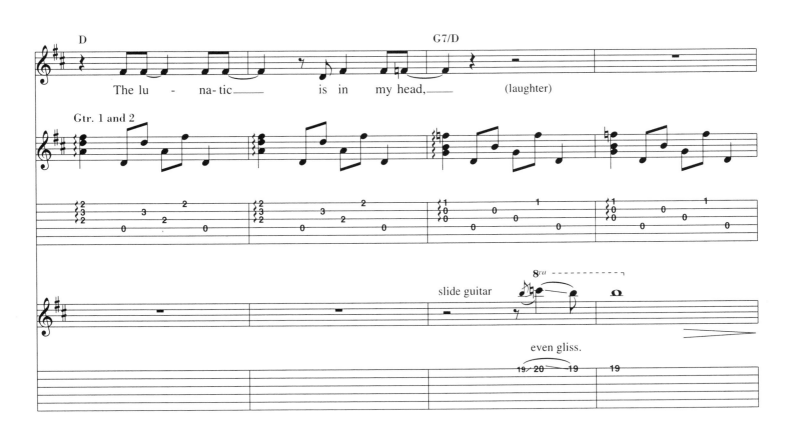

The lu - na - tic___ is in my head,___ (laughter)

Gtr. 1 and 2

slide guitar

even gliss.

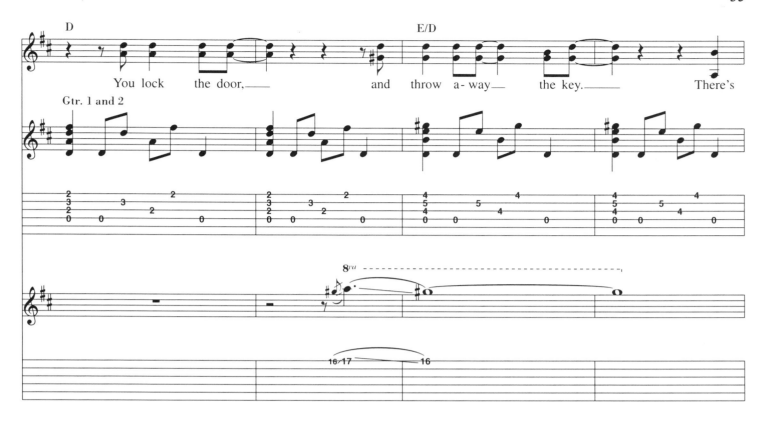

You lock the door,_____ and throw a-way_____ the key._____ There's

some-one in my head, but it's not me.

And if the cloud_____ bursts

36

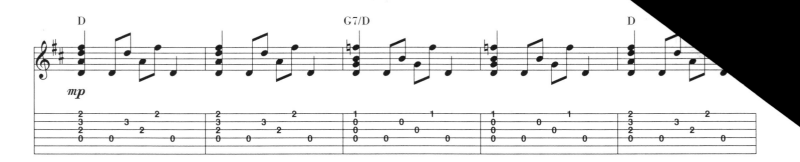

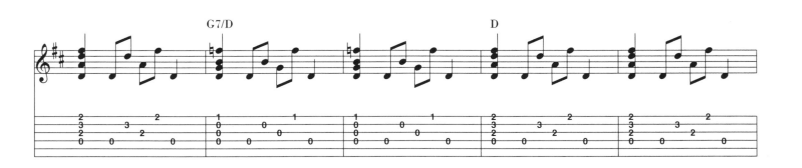

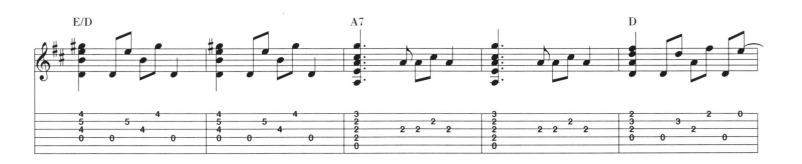

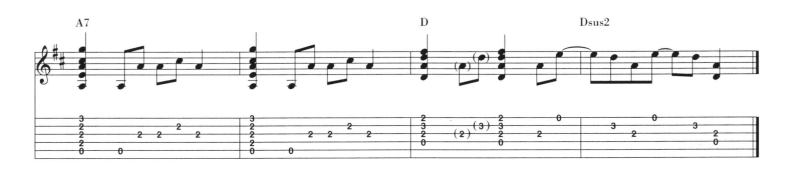

COMFORTABLY NUMB

Testo e Musica di Roger Waters, David Gilmour

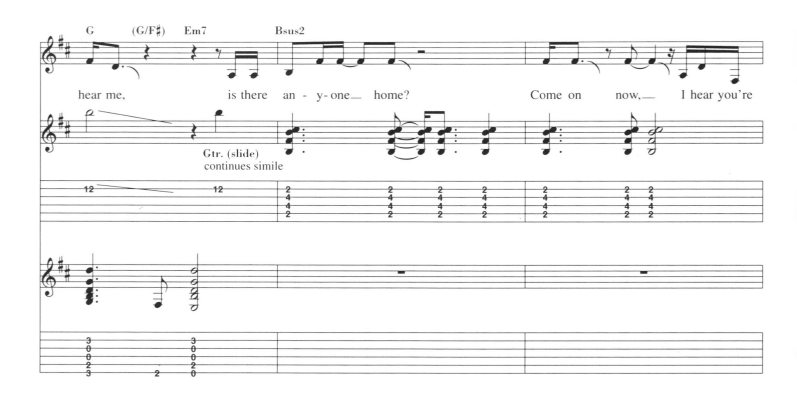

feel-ing down,___ well, I can ease your pain___ and get you on your feet a-gain.___

Re - lax, I'll need some in - for - ma - tion first, with slide guitar fill 1

just the ba - sic facts,___ can you show me where it hurts?

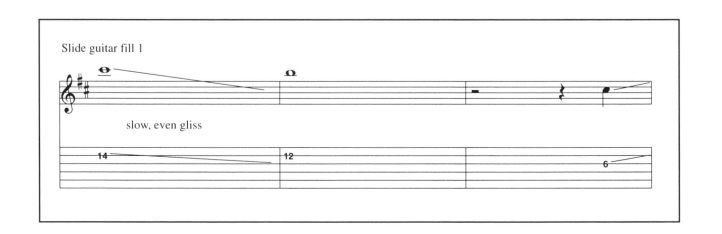

Slide guitar fill 1

slow, even gliss

Pre-chorus

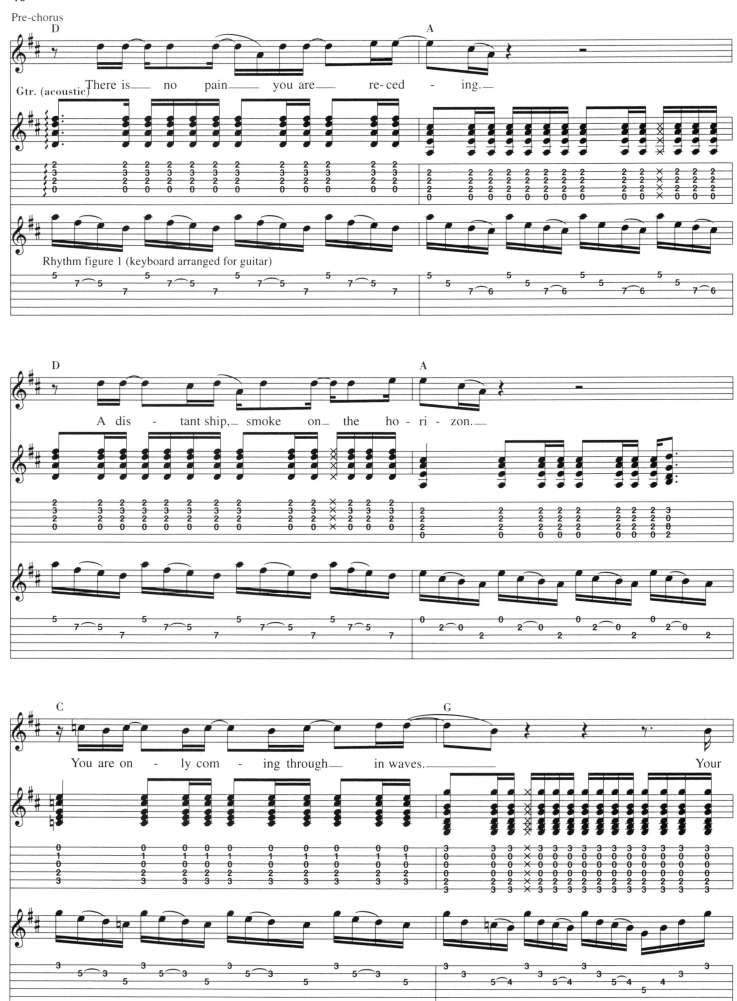

Gtr. (acoustic) There is— no pain— you are— re-ced - ing.—

Rhythm figure 1 (keyboard arranged for guitar)

A dis - tant ship,— smoke on— the ho - ri - zon.—

You are on - ly com - ing through— in waves.—————————— Your

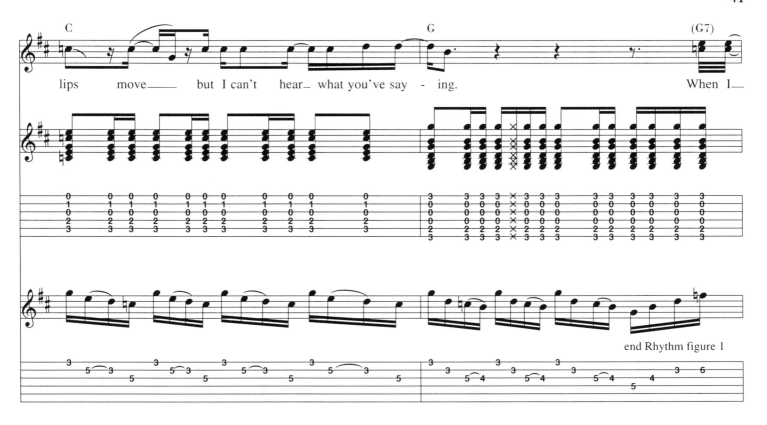

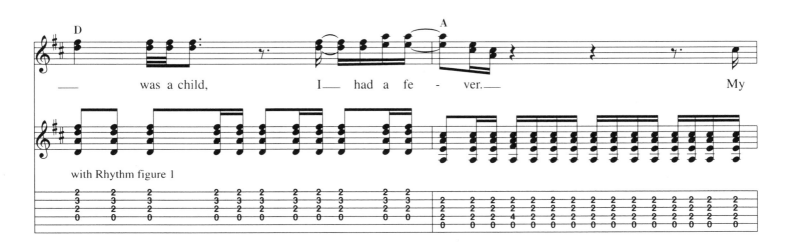

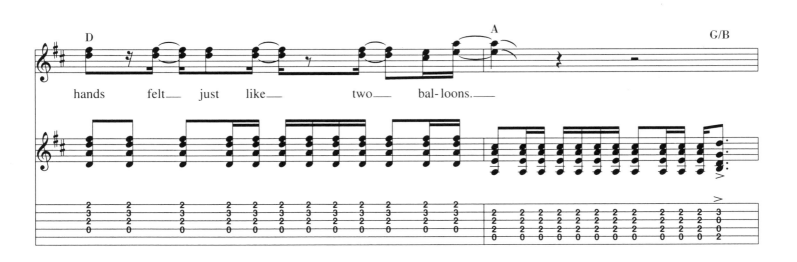

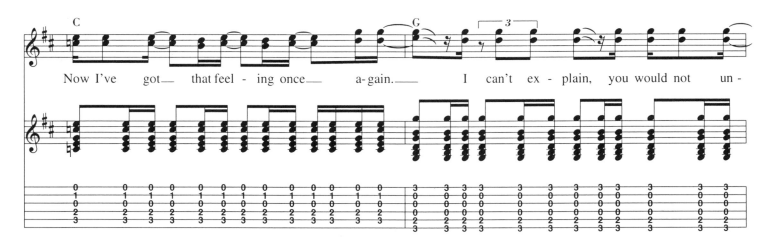

Now I've got— that feel - ing once— a-gain.— I can't ex - plain, you would not un-

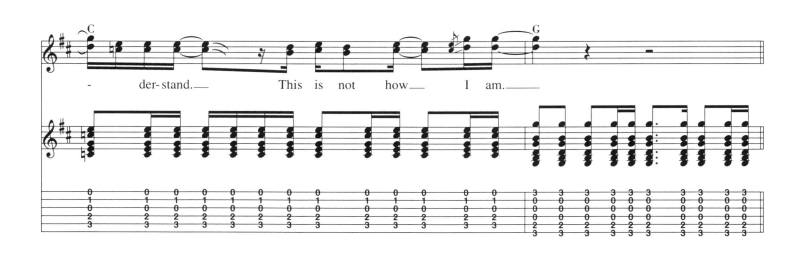

- der-stand.— This is not how— I am.—

Chorus

I_____ have be-come— com-f'rta- bly numb.—

Gtr. 1 (Solo)

rake

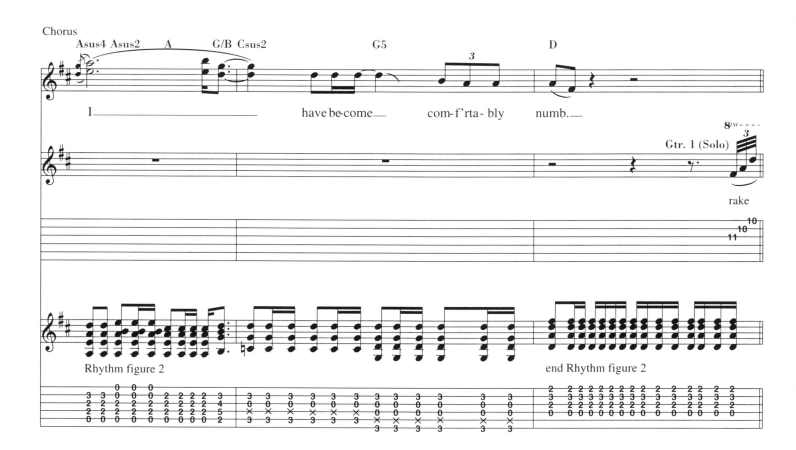

Rhythm figure 2

end Rhythm figure 2

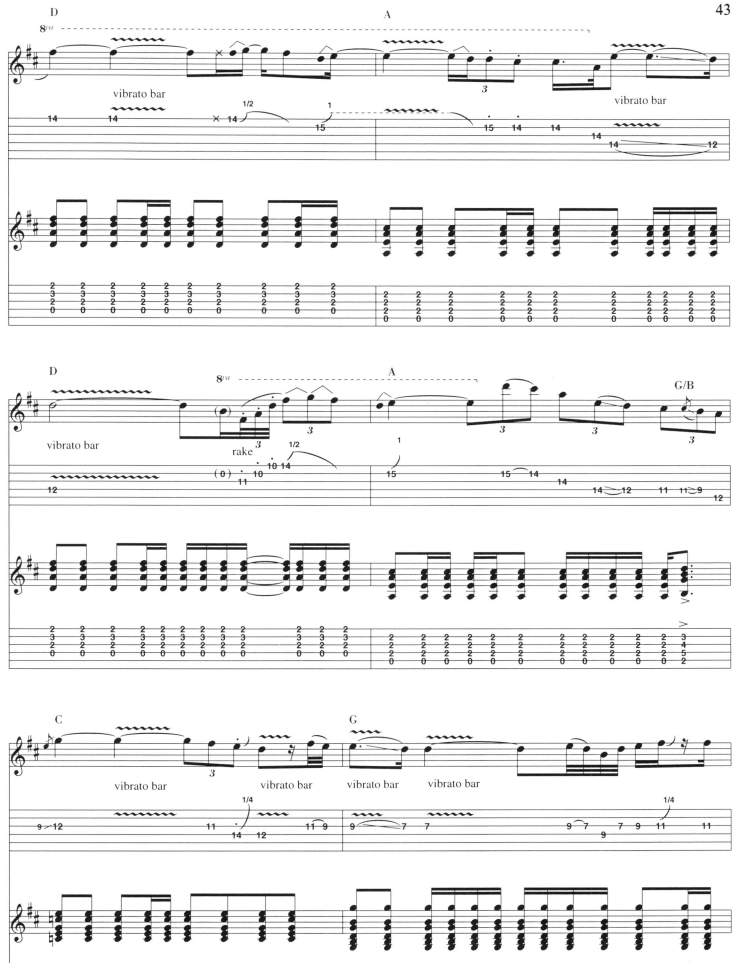

it now. The child is grown, the dream is gone.

(use for last bar of Rhythm figure 1)

Chorus

I have be-come com-f'rta-bly numb.

with Rhythm figure 2

Gtr. (electric)

divisi   with distortion

Gtr. 2 (Solo)

with feedback at
octave and twelfth

rake

BREATHE

Testo e Musica di Roger Waters, David Gilmour, Rick Wright

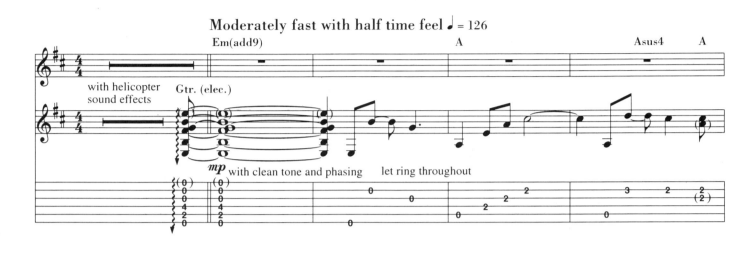

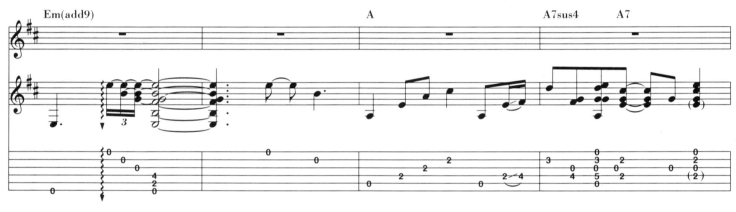

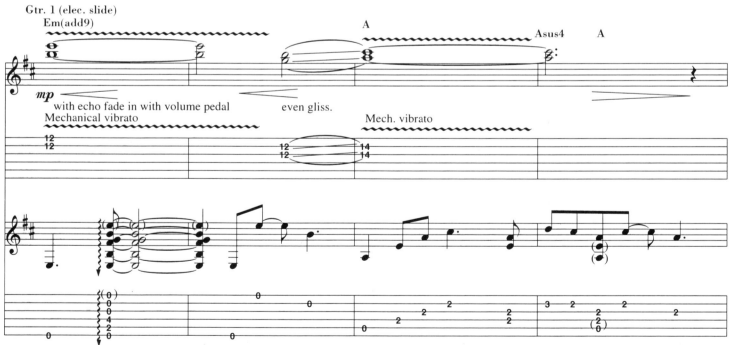

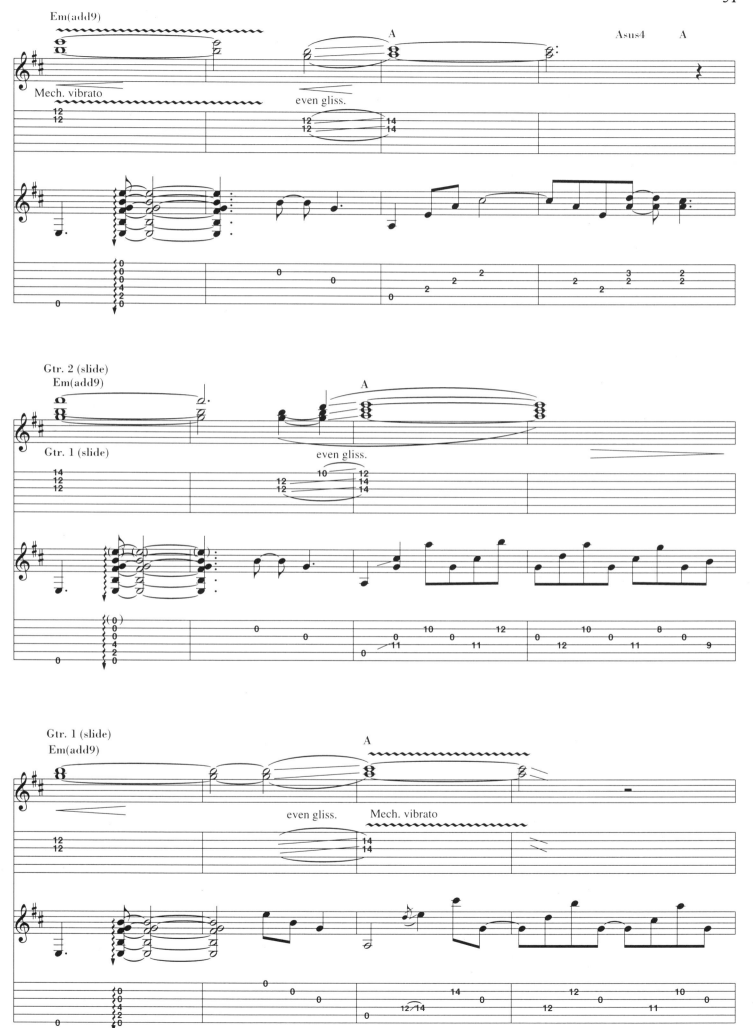

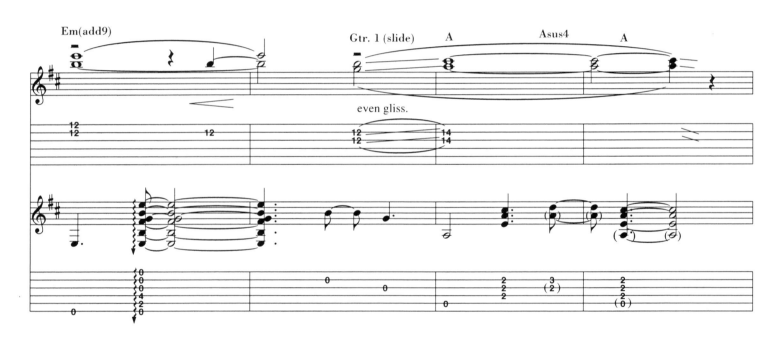

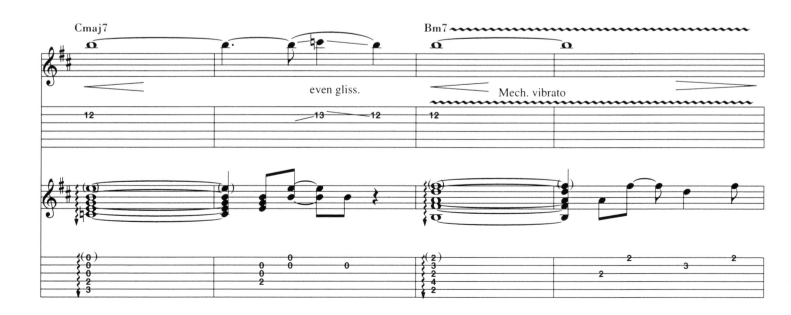

ECLIPSE

Testo e Musica di Roger Waters

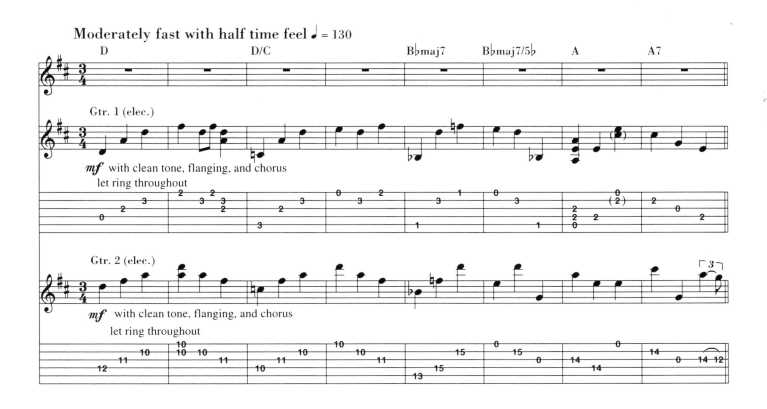

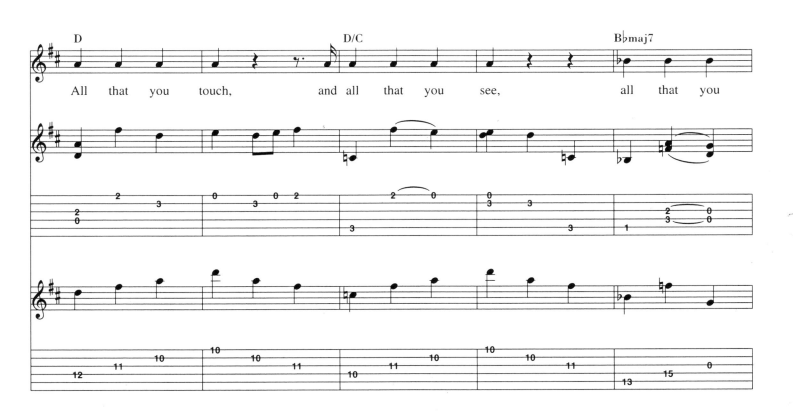

58

GOODBYE BLUE SKY

Testo e Musica di Roger Waters

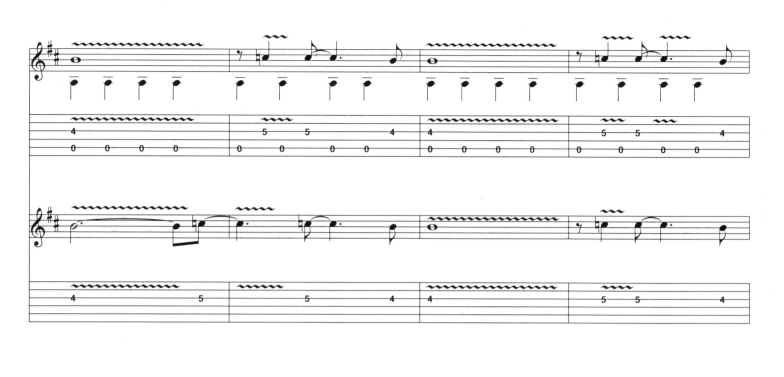

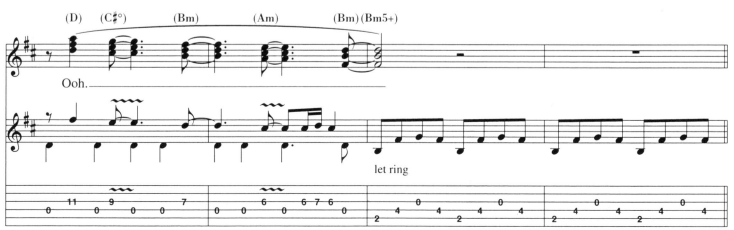

Gtr. 1 and 2 double part

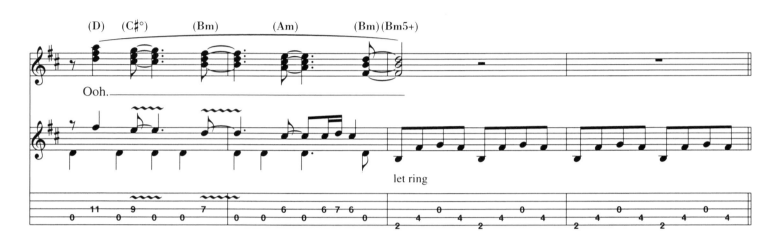

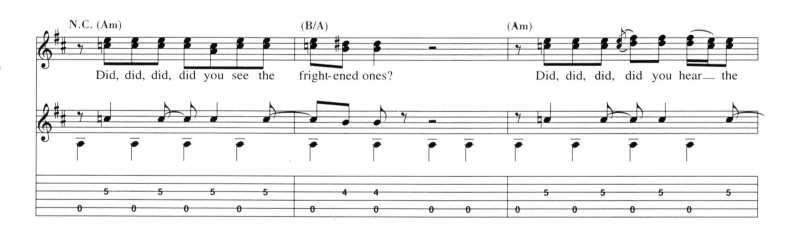

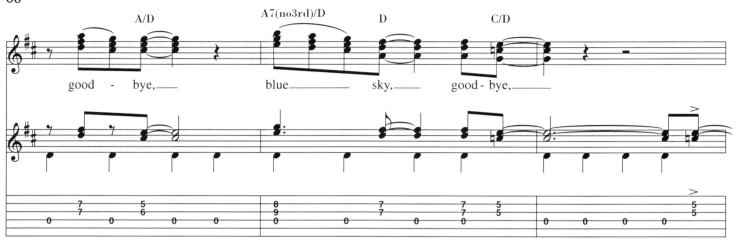

good - bye,_____ blue_____ sky,_____ good - bye,_____

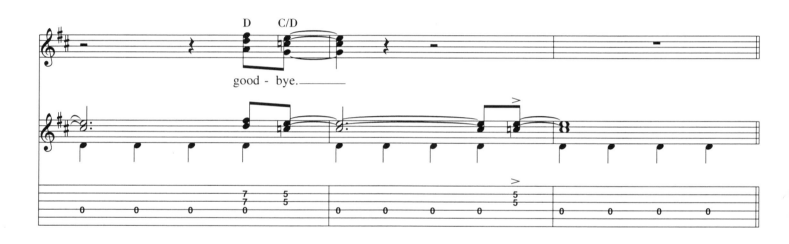

good - bye._____

N.C. (D)

fade out

HAVE A CIGAR

Testo e Musica di Roger Waters

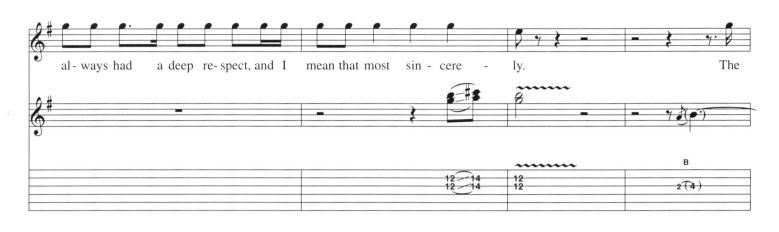

al-ways had a deep re-spect, and I mean that most sin-cere - ly. The

band is just fan-tas-tic, that is real-ly what I think, oh,— by the way, which one's

with Rhythm figure 5

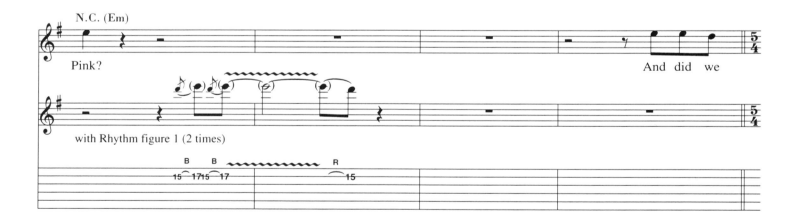

Pink? And did we

with Rhythm figure 1 (2 times)

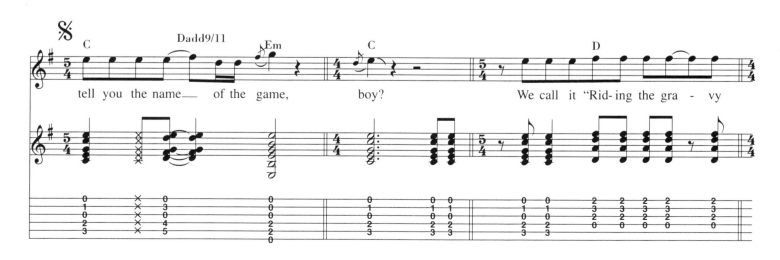

tell you the name— of the game, boy? We call it "Rid-ing the gra - vy

count.___ Ev-'ry-bod- y else is just green,_____ have__

with Rhythm figure 1 (4 1/2 times)

__ you seen the chart?___ It's a hell of a__ start,__ it could be made in-to a mon - ster, if we

with Rhythm figure 5

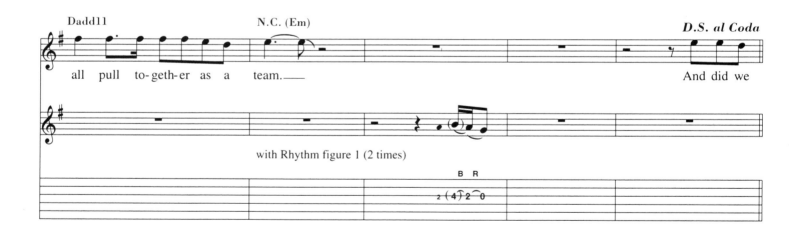

Dadd11   N.C. (Em)   **D.S. al Coda**

all pull to- geth-er as a team.___ And did we

with Rhythm figure 1 (2 times)

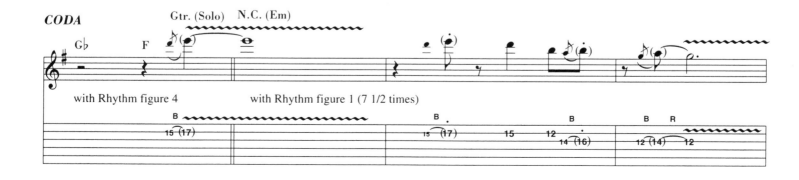

CODA

Gtr. (Solo)   N.C. (Em)

with Rhythm figure 4   with Rhythm figure 1 (7 1/2 times)

* Trap the 3rd string while bending the 2nd string.

** Trap the 2nd string while bending the 1st string.

HEY YOU

Testo e Musica di Roger Waters

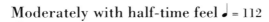

Moderately with half-time feel ♩ = 112

Intro

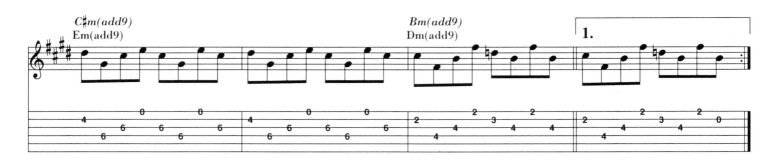

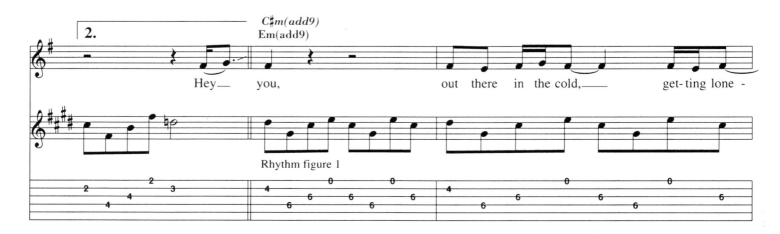

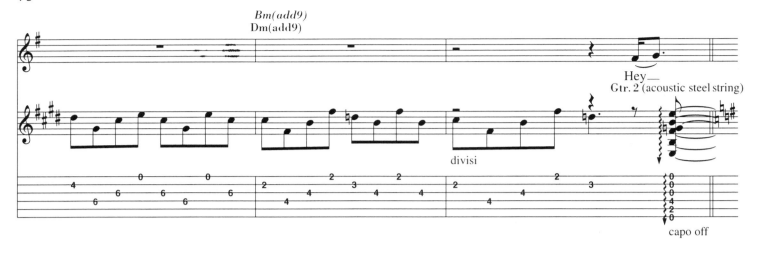

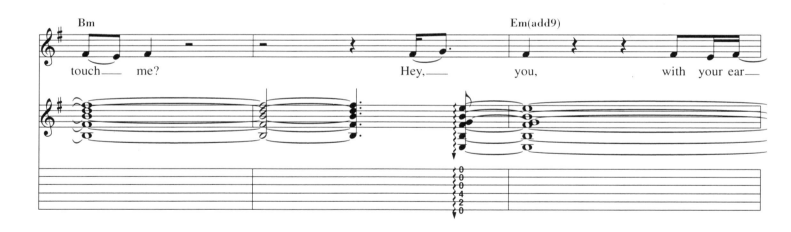

Hey, you!___ Would you help me to car-ry the stone?___

O - pen your heart, I'm com-ing home.___

Gtr. 1 (elec.)

with distortion

Gtr. (Solo)
Gtr. 2 (elec.)

Gtr. 1 (elec.)
Solo figure 1

Gtr. 3 (elec.)

hold bend   slow, even release   hold bend   with feedback at octave
slow, even release

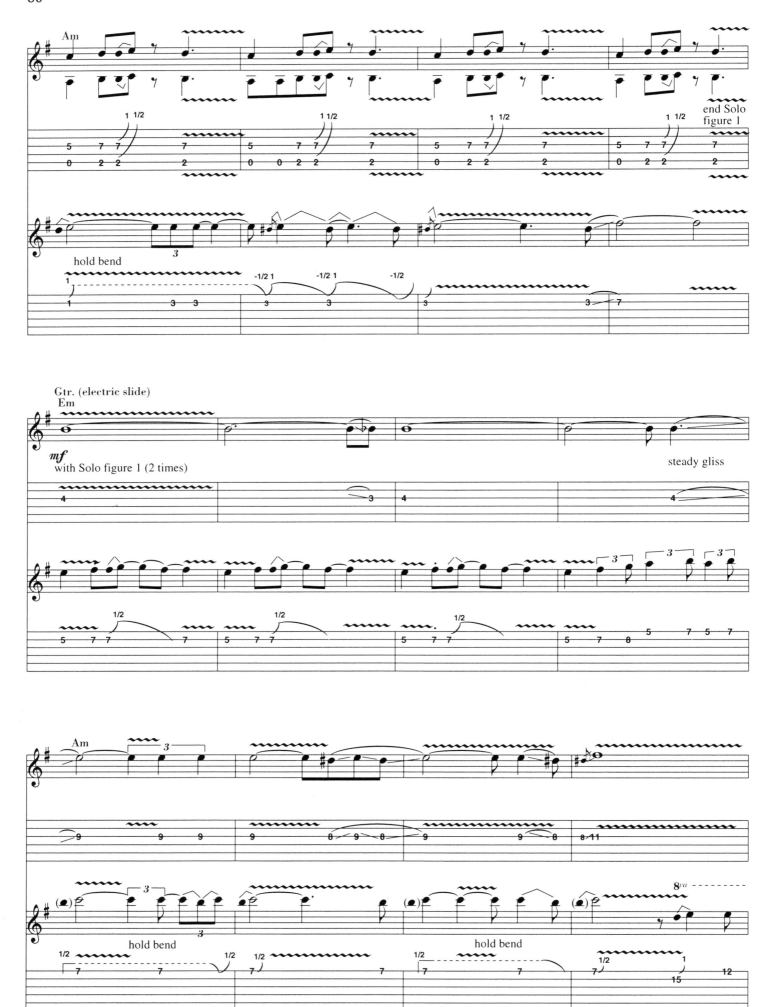

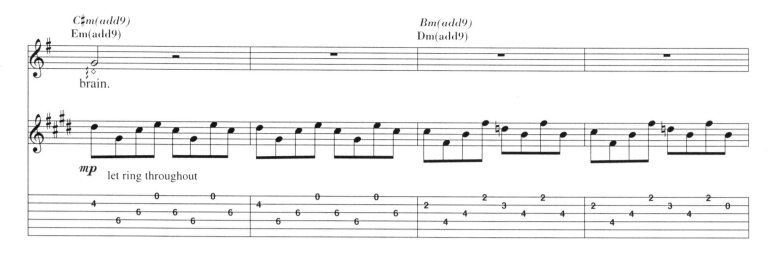

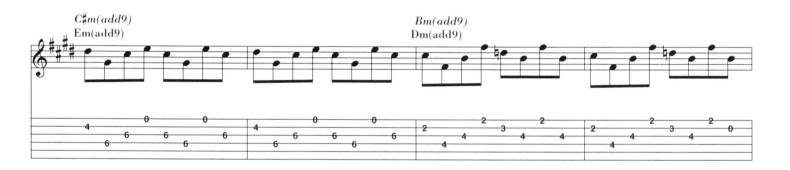

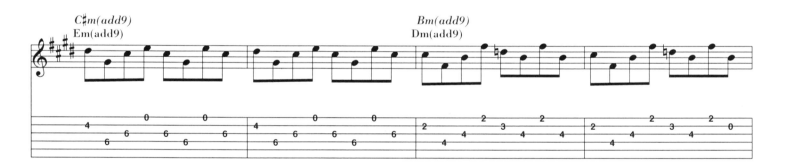

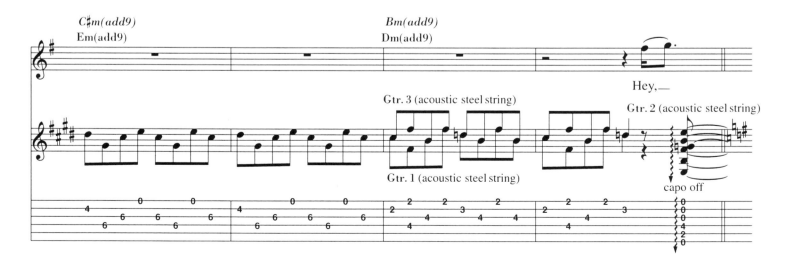

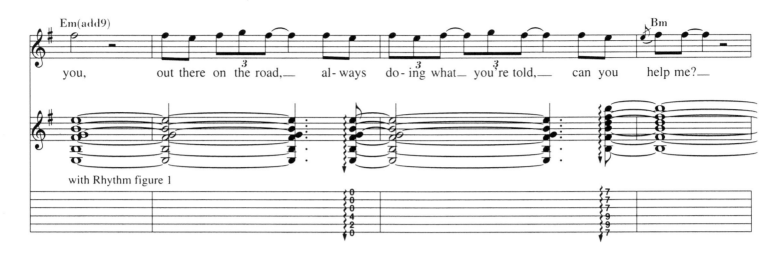

with Rhythm figure 1

you, out there on the road,— al-ways do-ing what— you're told,— can you help me?—

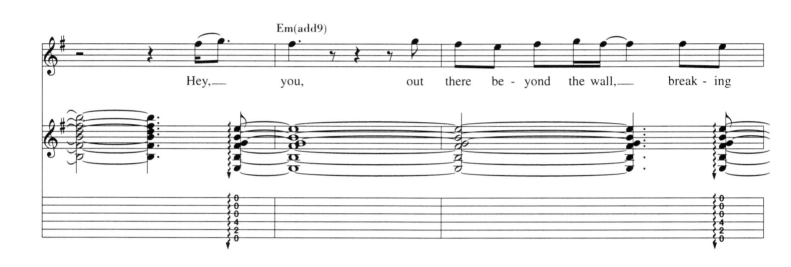

Hey,— you, out there be-yond the wall,— break-ing

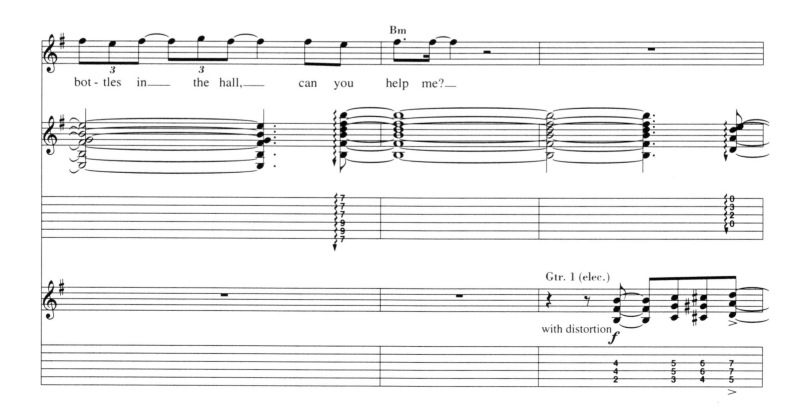

bot-tles in— the hall,— can you help me?—

Gtr. 1 (elec.)

with distortion

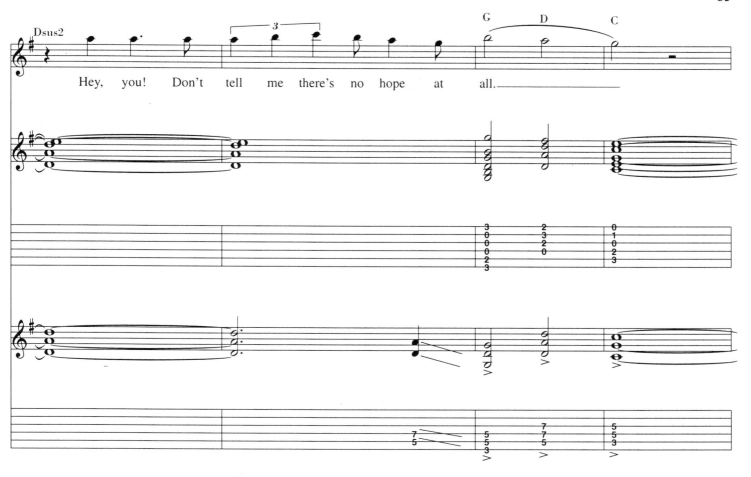

Hey, you! Don't tell me there's no hope at all.

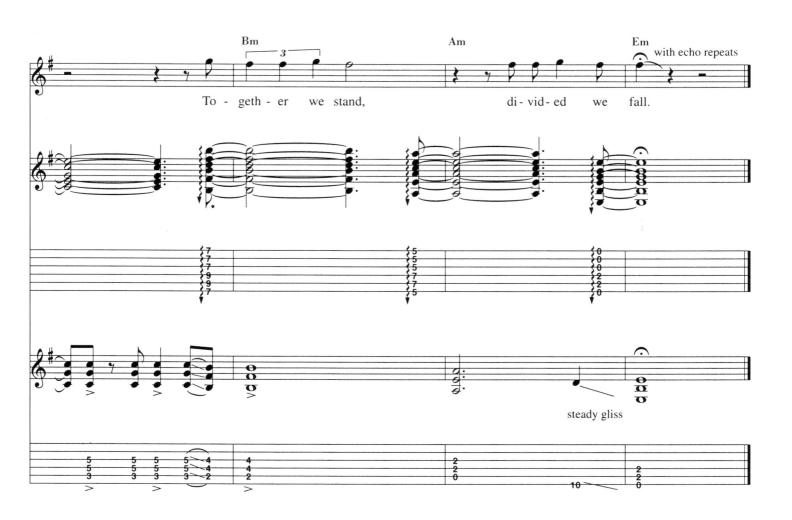

To - geth - er we stand, di - vid - ed we fall.

with echo repeats

steady gliss

IF

Testo e Musica di Roger Waters

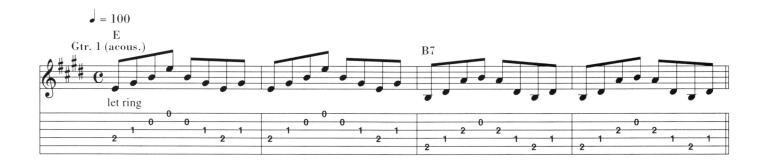

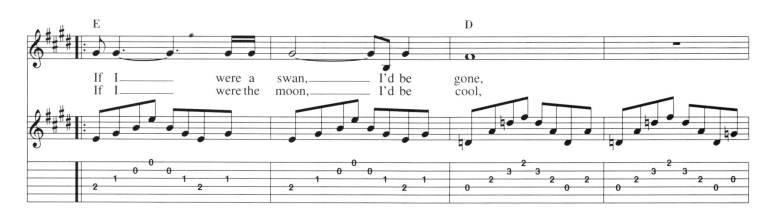

IS THERE ANYBODY OUT THERE?

Testo e Musica di Roger Waters

Slowly ♩ = 119

N.C. (A5)

television and traffic sound effects
for approximately 10 seconds

Is there an - y - bod - y out there?

synthesizer drone *mp*

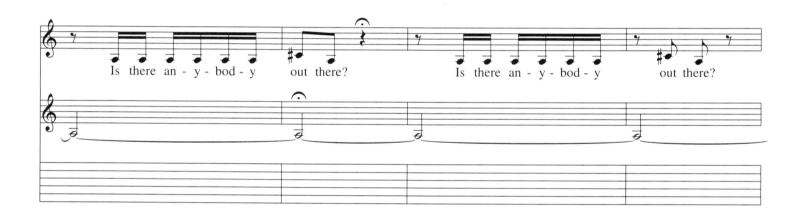

Is there an - y - bod - y out there?

Is there an - y - bod - y out there?

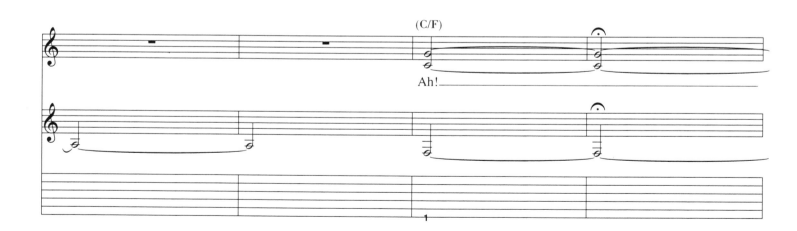

(C/F)

Ah!

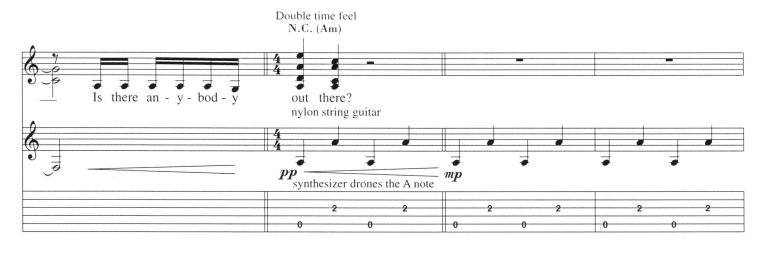

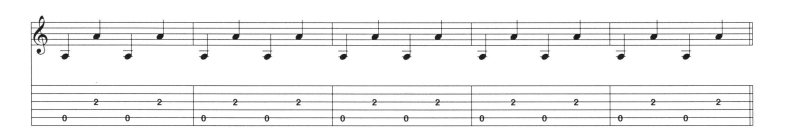

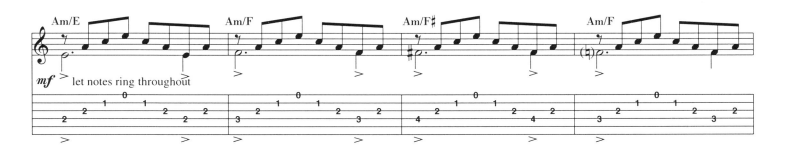

MONEY

Testo e Musica di Roger Waters

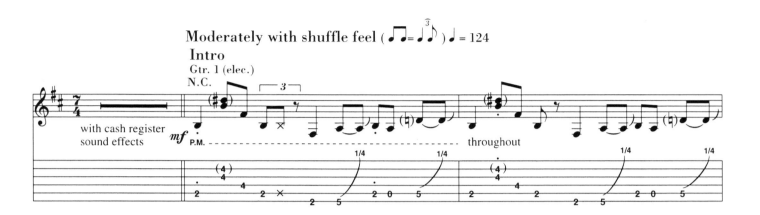

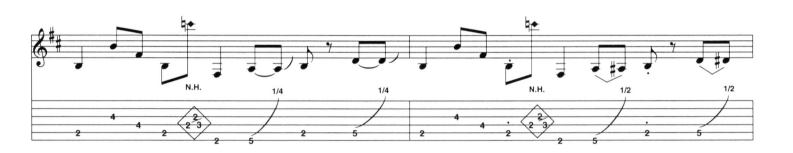

New car, cav-i-ar, four-star day-dream, think I'll buy me a foot-ball_____
high fi-del-i-ty first class trav-'ling set and I think I need a Lear_____
But if you ask for a rise it's no sur - - prise that they're giv - ing none a-

_____ team.
_____ jet.

* Play on verse 2 only
Saxophone solo

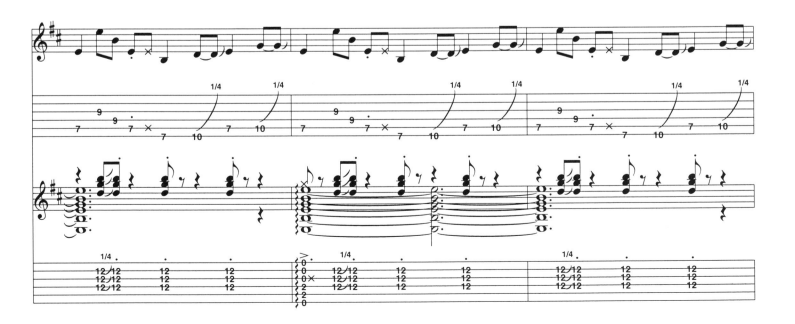

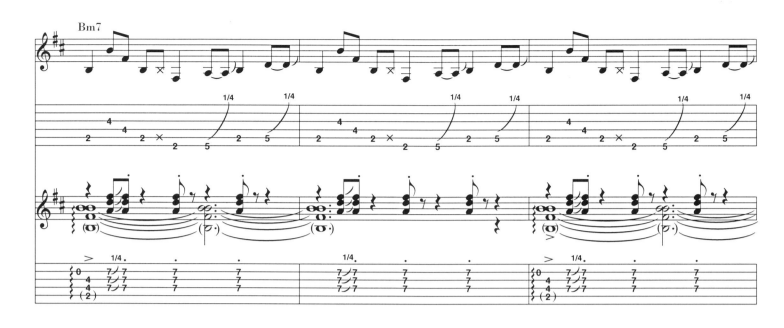

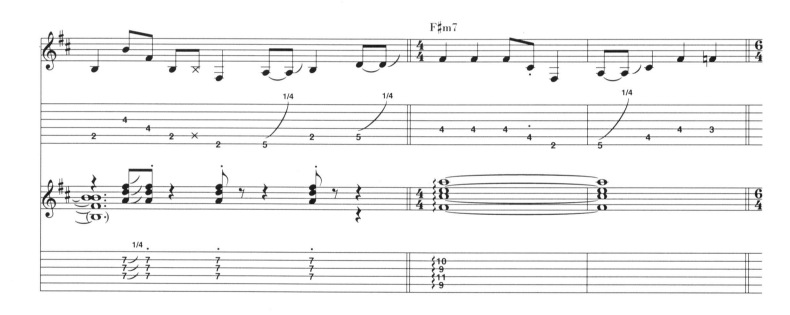

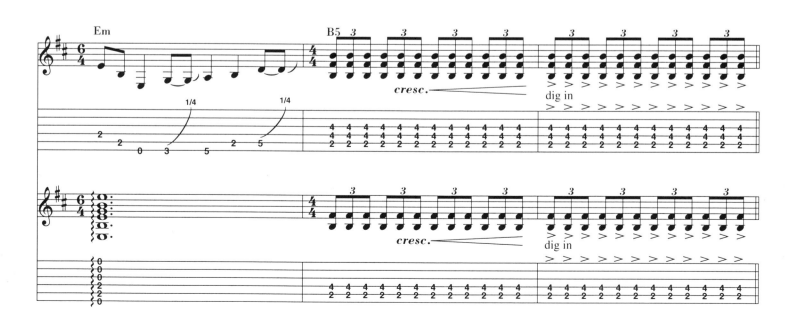

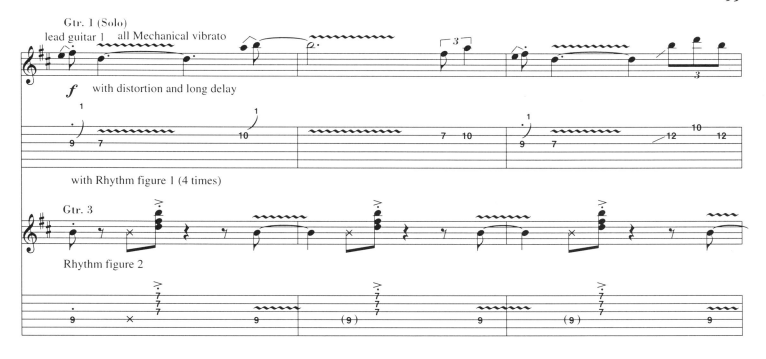

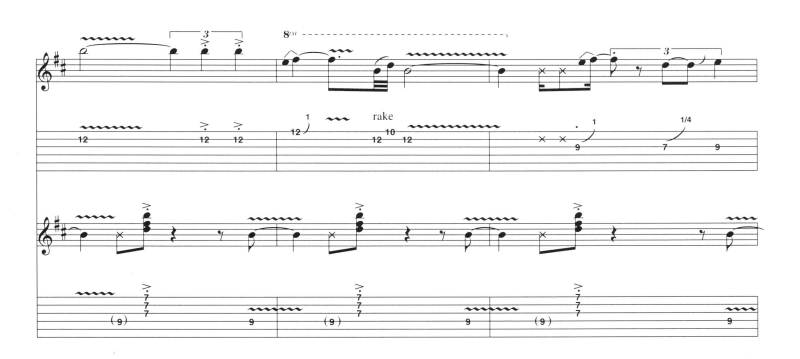

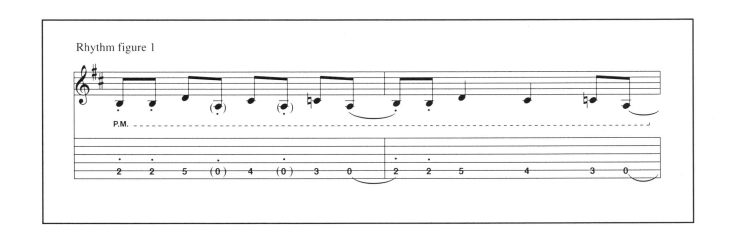

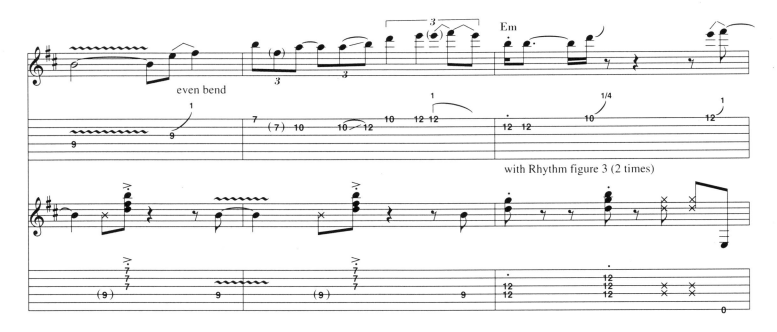

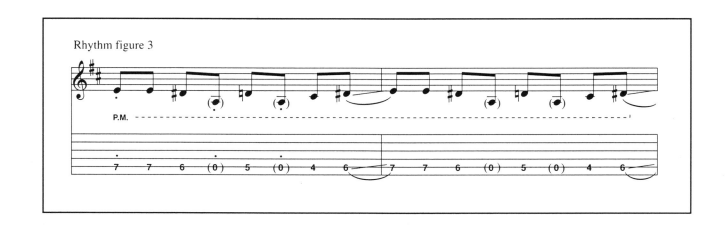

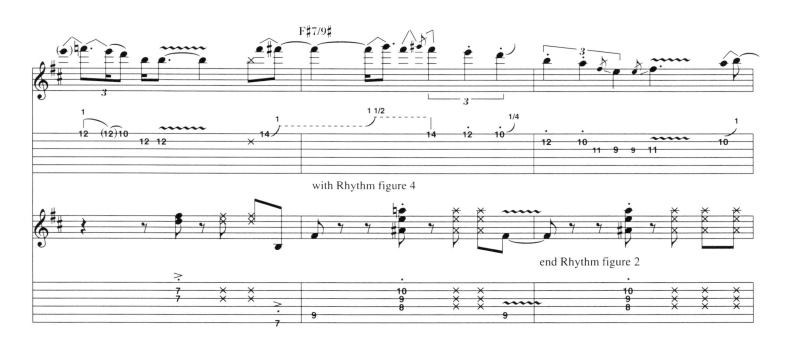

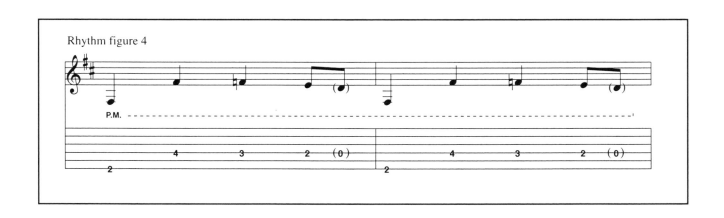

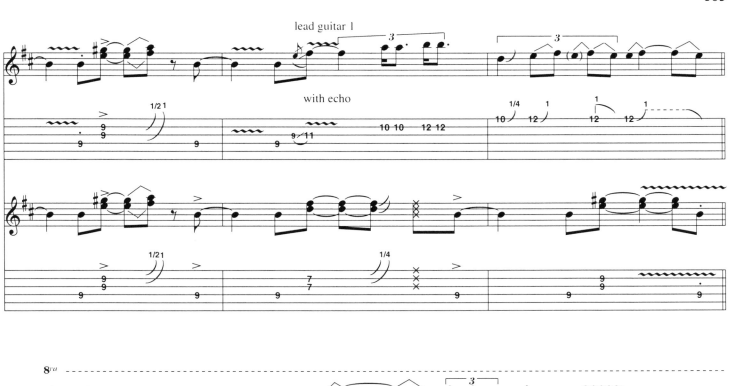

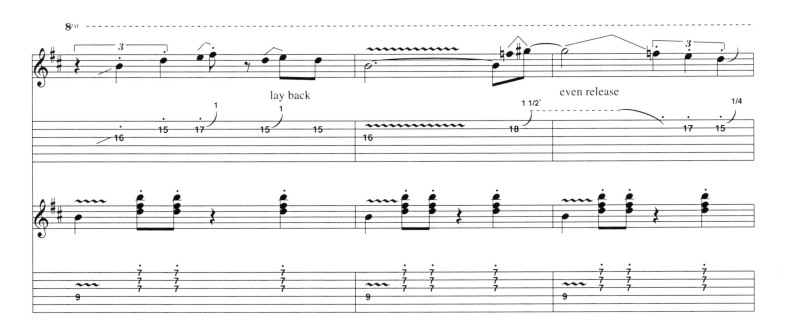

straight eights

Spoken: "I don't know;
I was drunk at the time."

hold bend

NOT NOW JOHN

Testo e Musica di Roger Waters

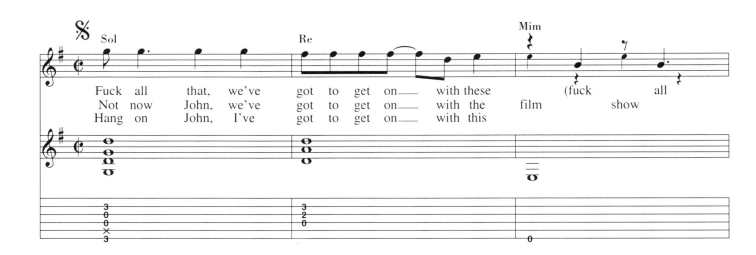

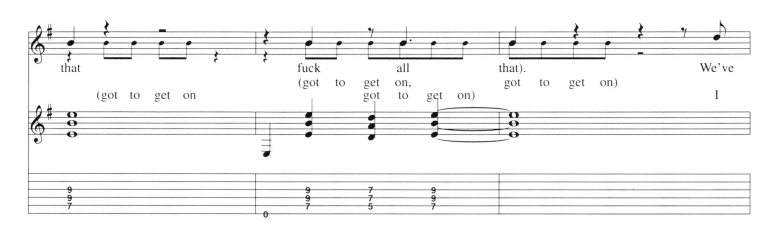

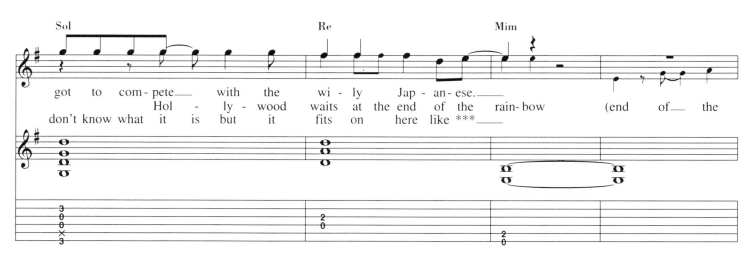

114

D. %: al ⊕, da A a B and sigue

ON THE TURNING AWAY

Testo e Musica di David Gilmour, Anthony Moore

On the turn-ing— a - way from the pale and

down - trod - den, and the words_ they say which we won't un - der-stand,

"Don't ac - cept that what's hap - pen-ing is just a case of oth-ers' suf - fer-ing,

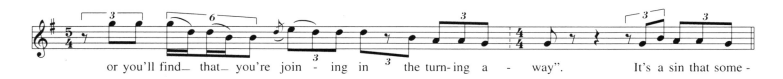

or you'll find_ that_ you're join - ing in the turn-ing a - way". It's a sin that some -

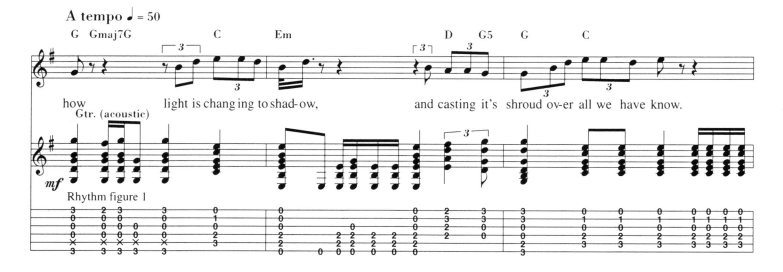

how light is chang-ing to shad-ow, and casting it's shroud ov-er all we have know.

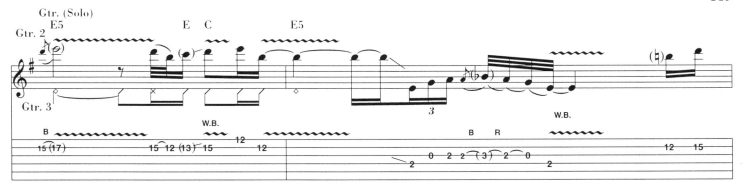

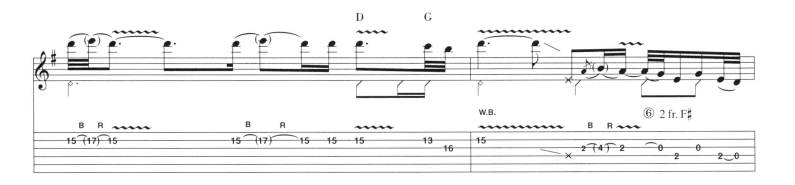

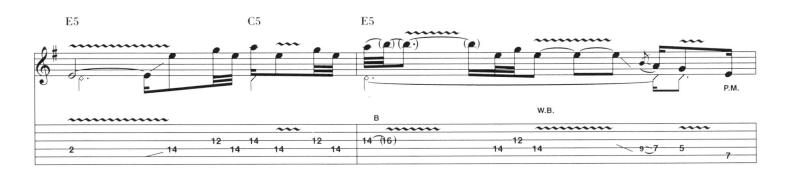

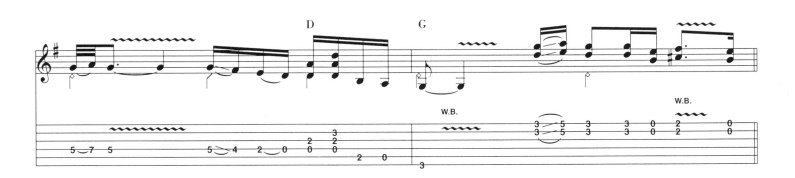

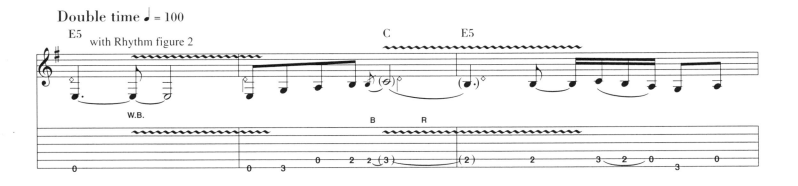

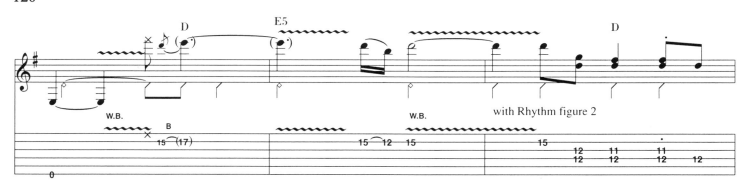

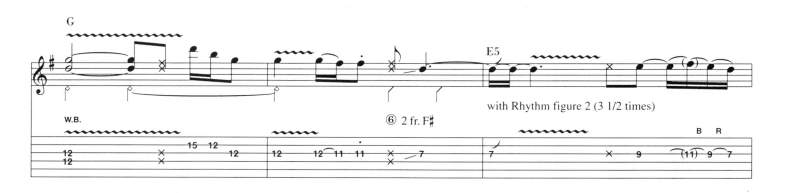

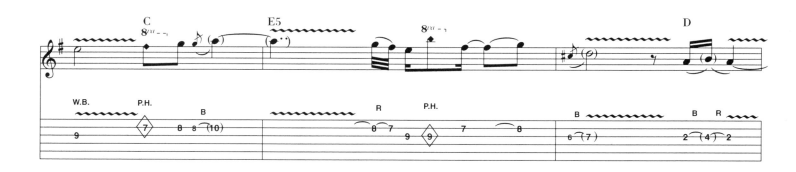

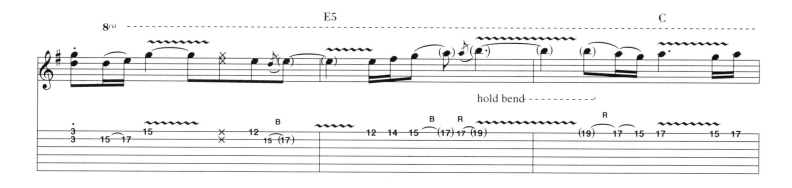

MOTHER

Testo e Musica di Roger Waters

Moderately with half-time feel ♪ = 134

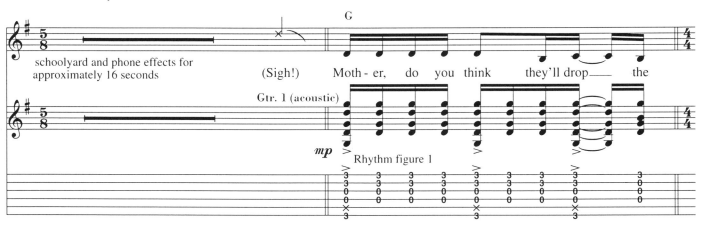

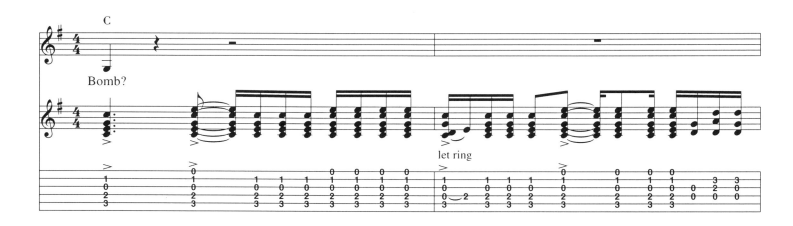

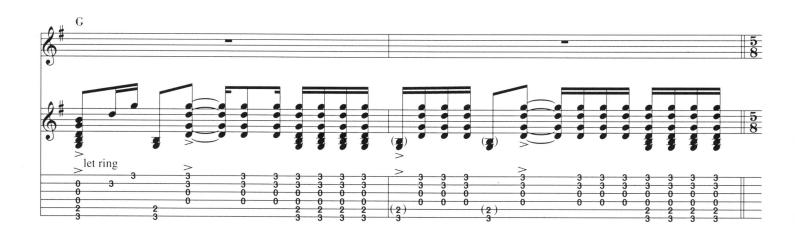

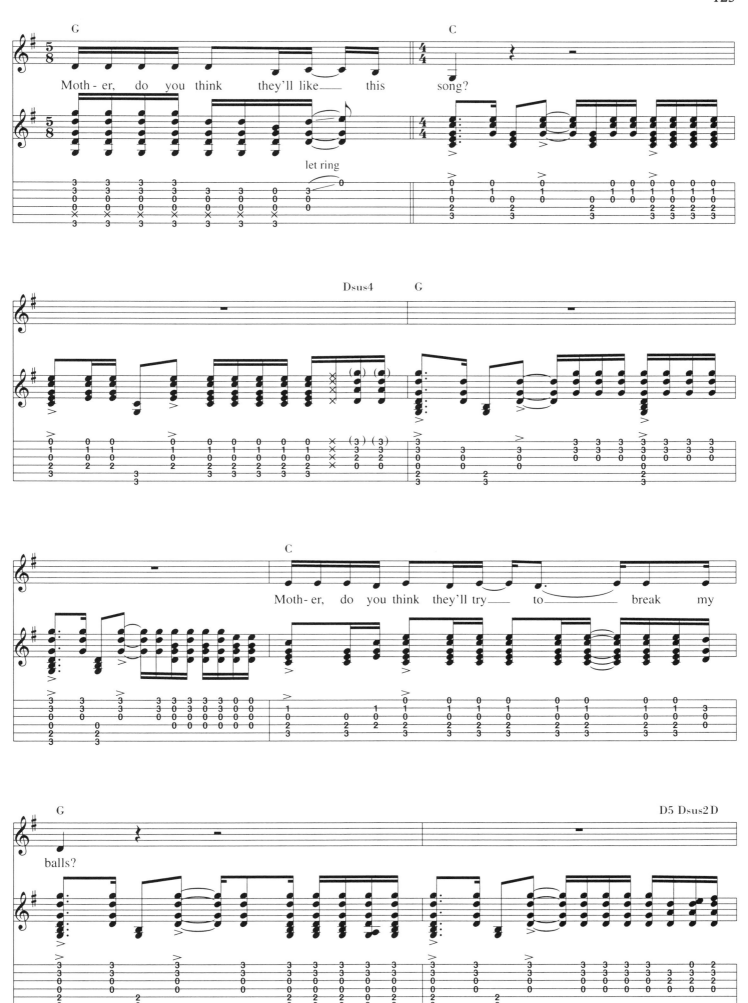

124

Hush now, ba-by, ba- - by don't you cry.

Ma-ma's gon-na make all_ of your night-mares come true
Ma-ma's gon-na check out_ all your girl-friends for you,

Ma-ma's gon-na put all_ of her fears in-to you,
Ma-ma's won't let_ an-y-one dir-ty get through,

Ma-ma's gon-na keep you right here un-der her_ wing. She
Ma-ma's_ gon-na wait up un-til you get_ in.

Gtr. 2 (acoustic)
with Rhythm fill 1
(Played by 12 string acoustic guitar).   (doubled by acoustic guitar 1)

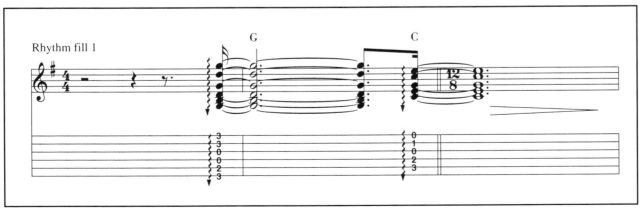

Rhythm fill 1

126

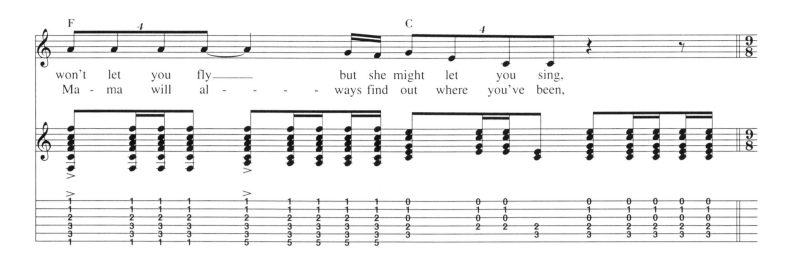

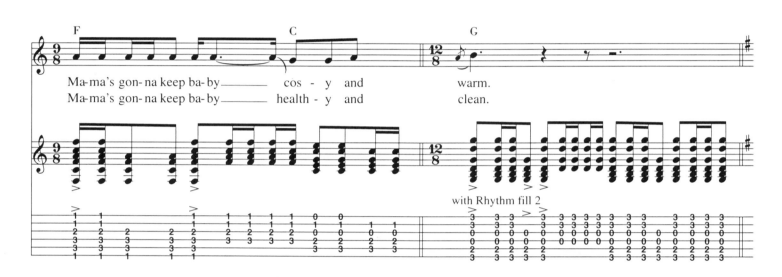

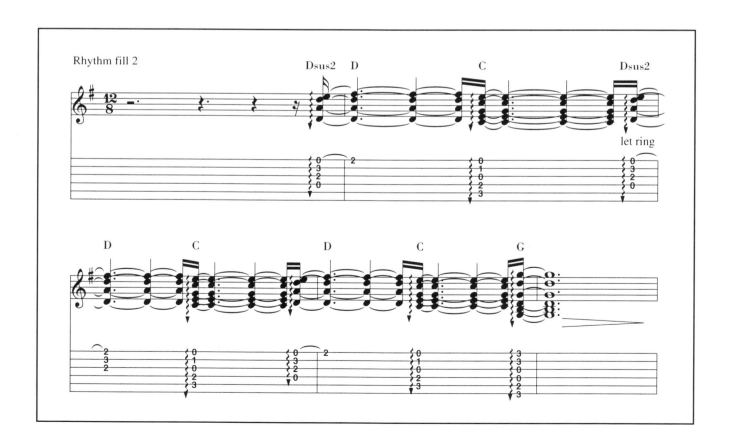

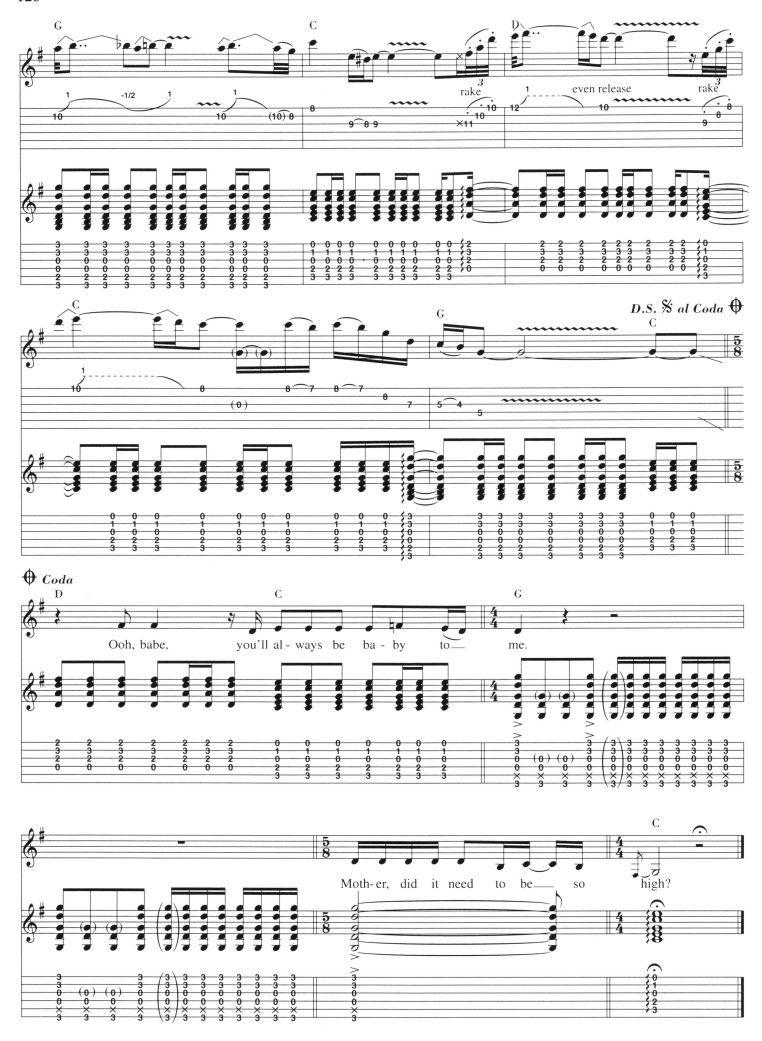

REMEMBER A DAY

Testo e Musica di Syd Barrett

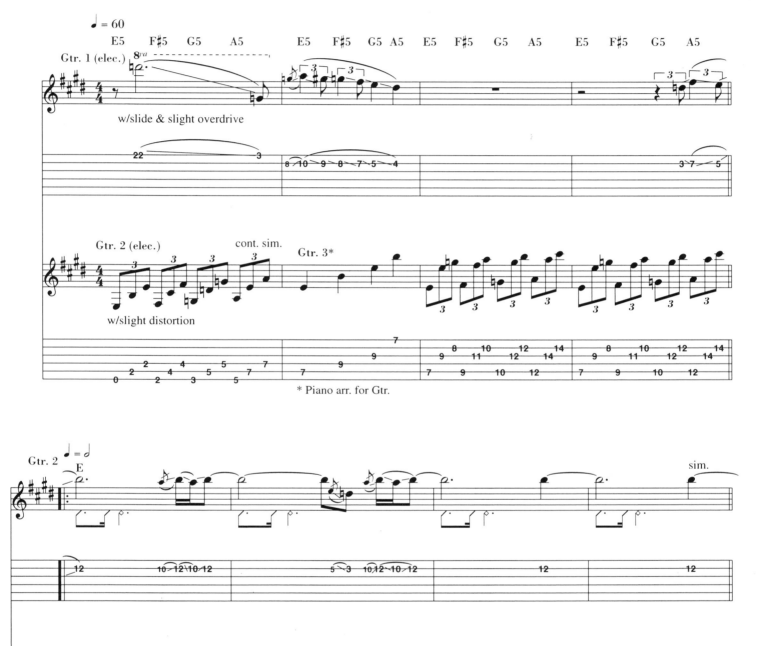

* Piano arr. for Gtr.

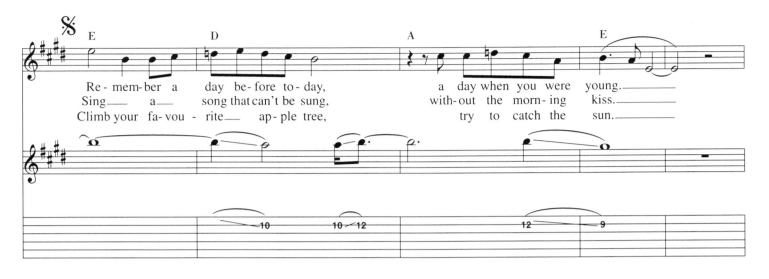

Re - mem-ber a   day be-fore to-day,   a day when you were   young.
Sing____ a____   song that can't be sung,   with-out the morn-ing   kiss.
Climb your fa-vou - rite____ ap-ple tree,   try to catch the   sun.

Free   to____   play a-long____ with time,   eve - ning nev - er
Queen   you shall   be____ if you wish,   look for your King.
Hide   from your   lit-tle bro - ther's gun,   dream your-self a -

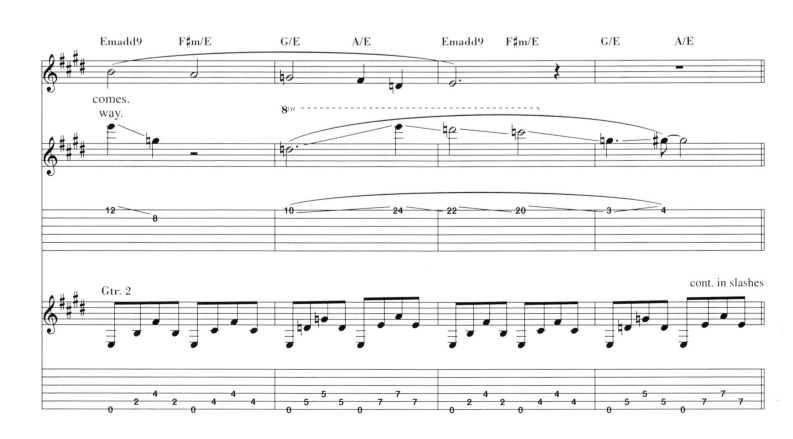

Emadd9   F♯m/E   G/E   A/E   Emadd9   F♯m/E   G/E   A/E

comes.
way.

Gtr. 2   cont. in slashes

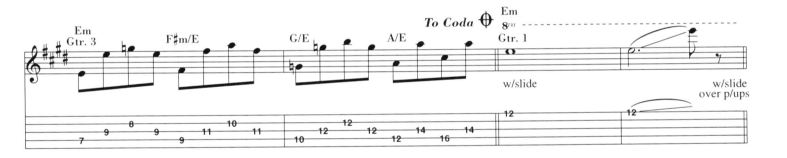

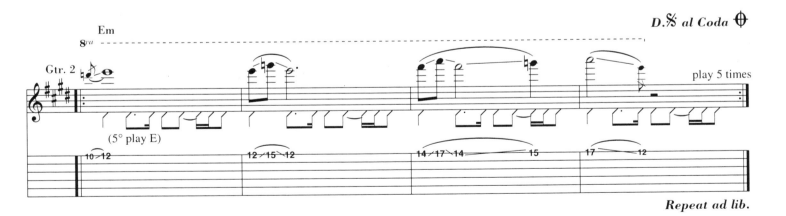

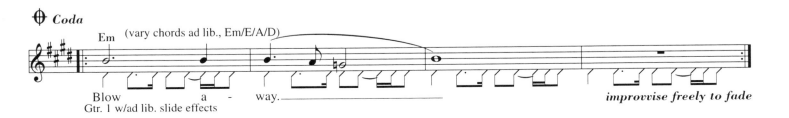

SEE EMILY PLAY

Testo e Musica di Syd Barrett

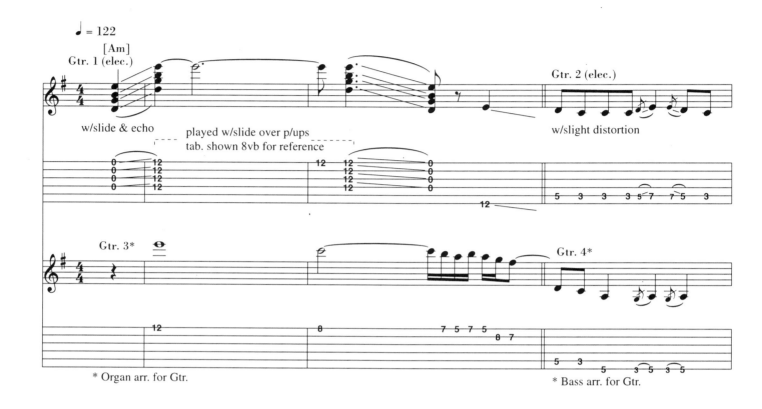

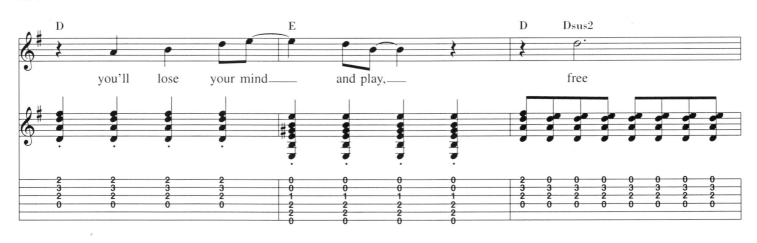

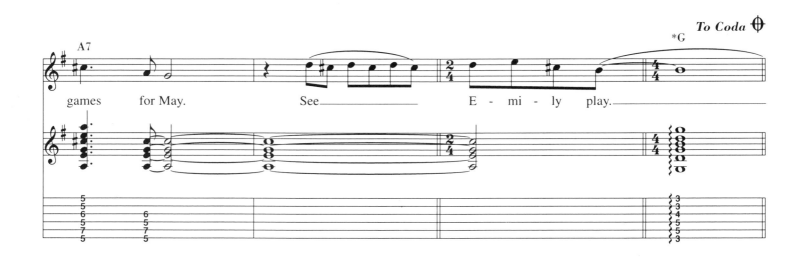

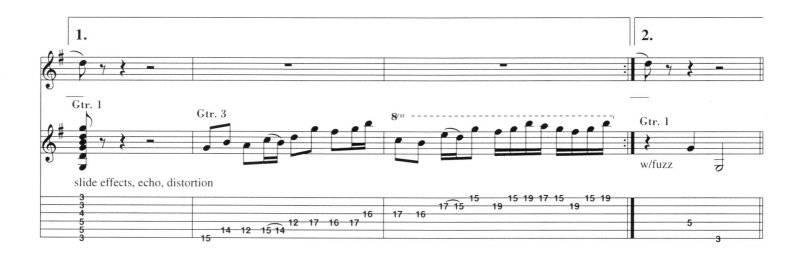

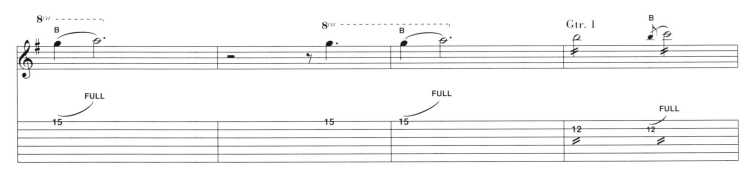

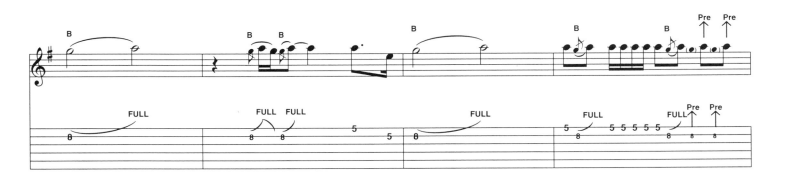

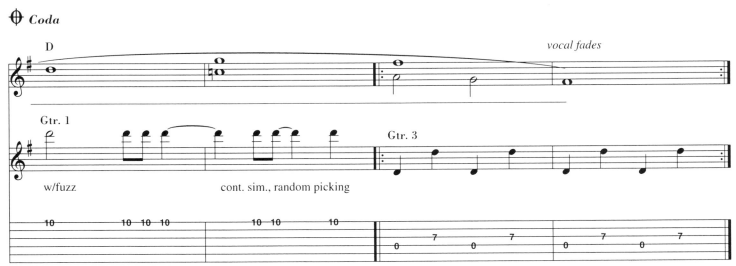

Repeat to fade

SHINE ON YOU CRAZY DIAMOND (PART V)

Testo e Musica di Roger Waters

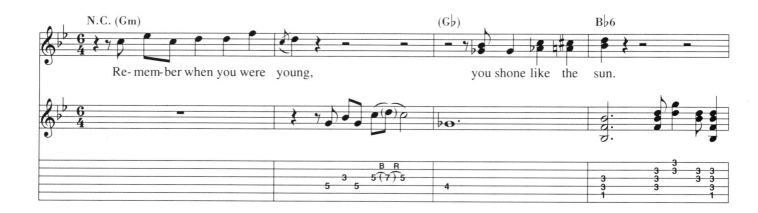

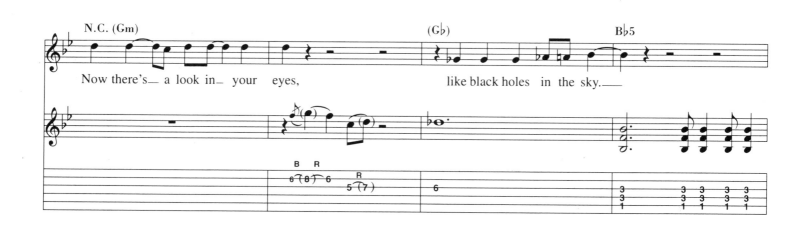

138

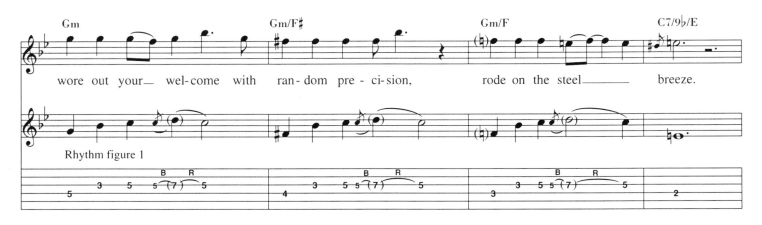

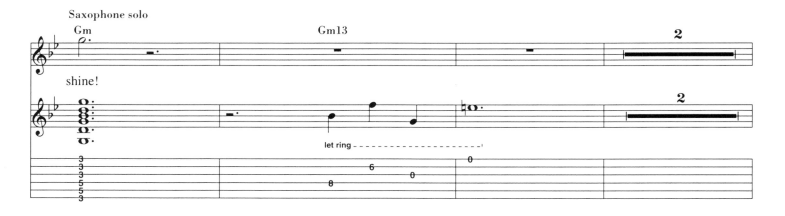

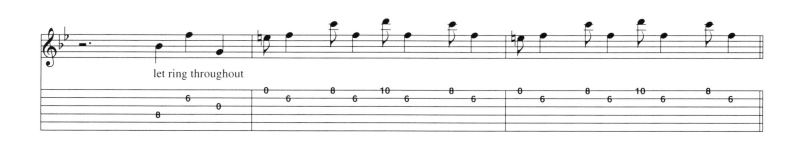

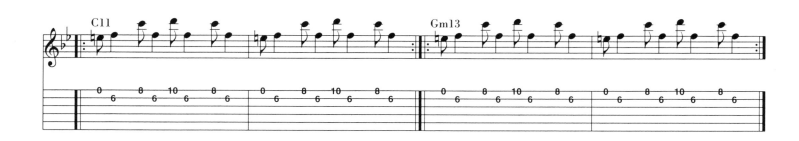

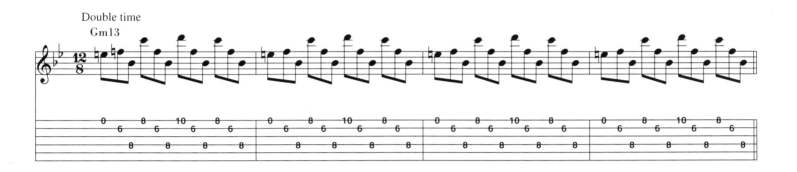

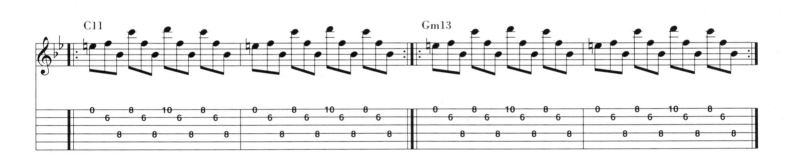

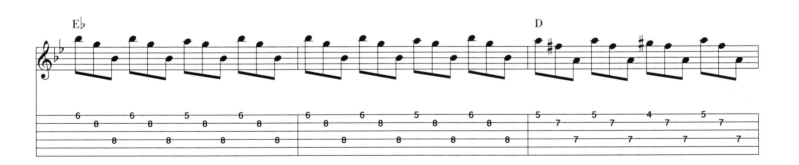

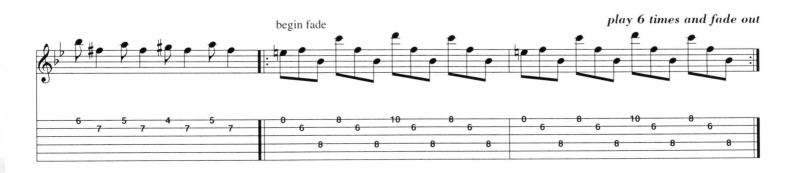

WISH YOU WERE HERE

Testo e Musica di Roger Waters, David Gilmour

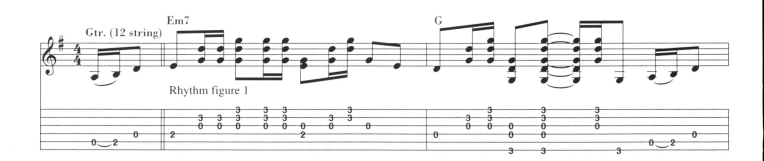

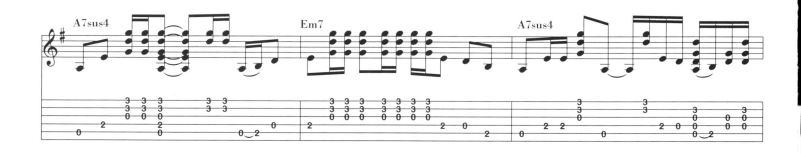

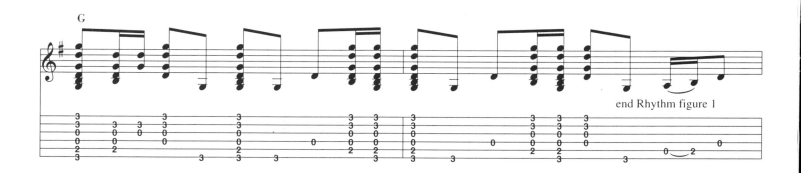

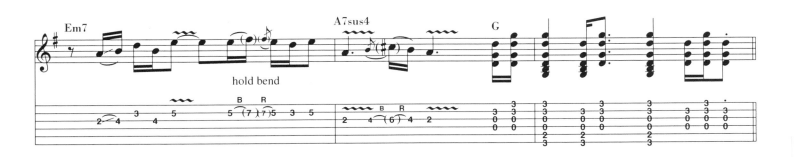

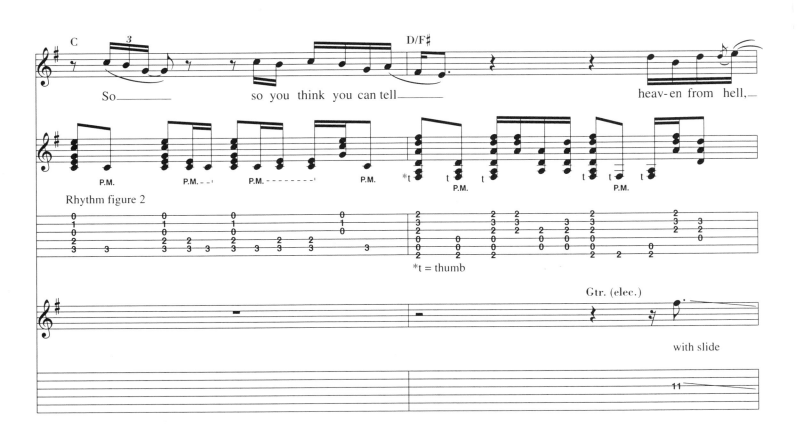

Tune to open G: ⑥ = D ⑤ = G ④ = D ③ = G ② = B ① = D

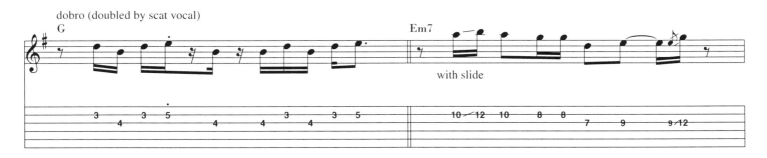

dobro (doubled by scat vocal)

with slide

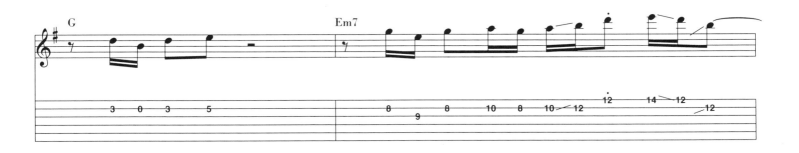

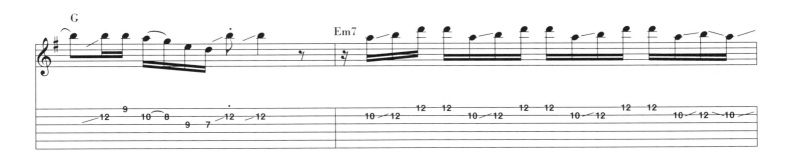

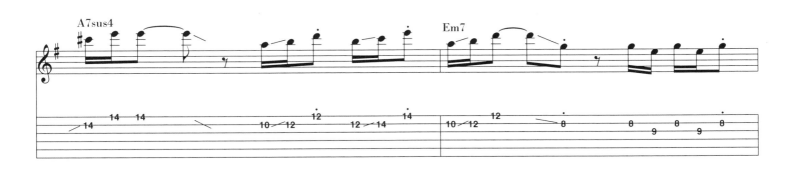

begin fade

fade into sound effects

with Rhythm figure 1 (first 8 bars)

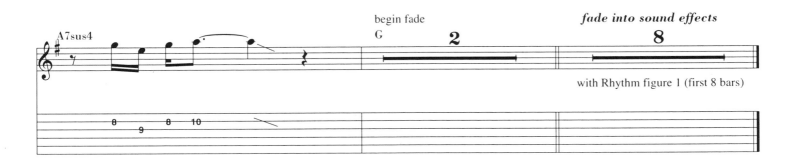

WELCOME TO THE MACHINE

Testo e Musica di Roger Waters

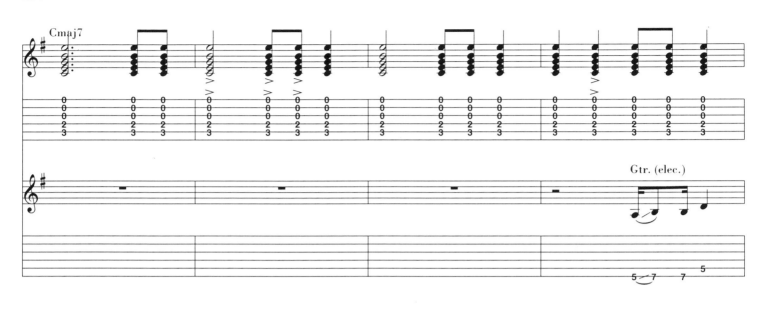

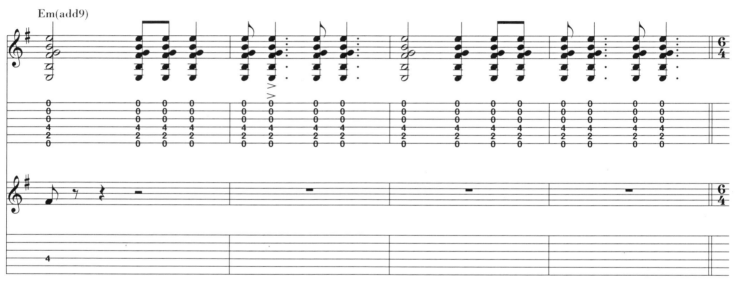

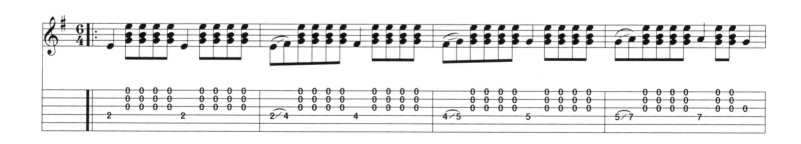

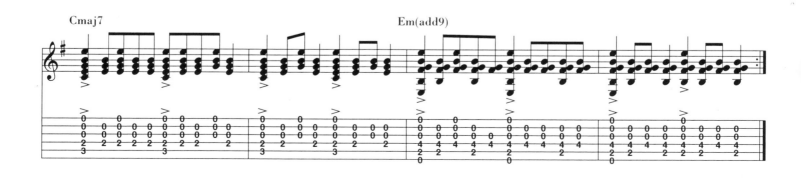

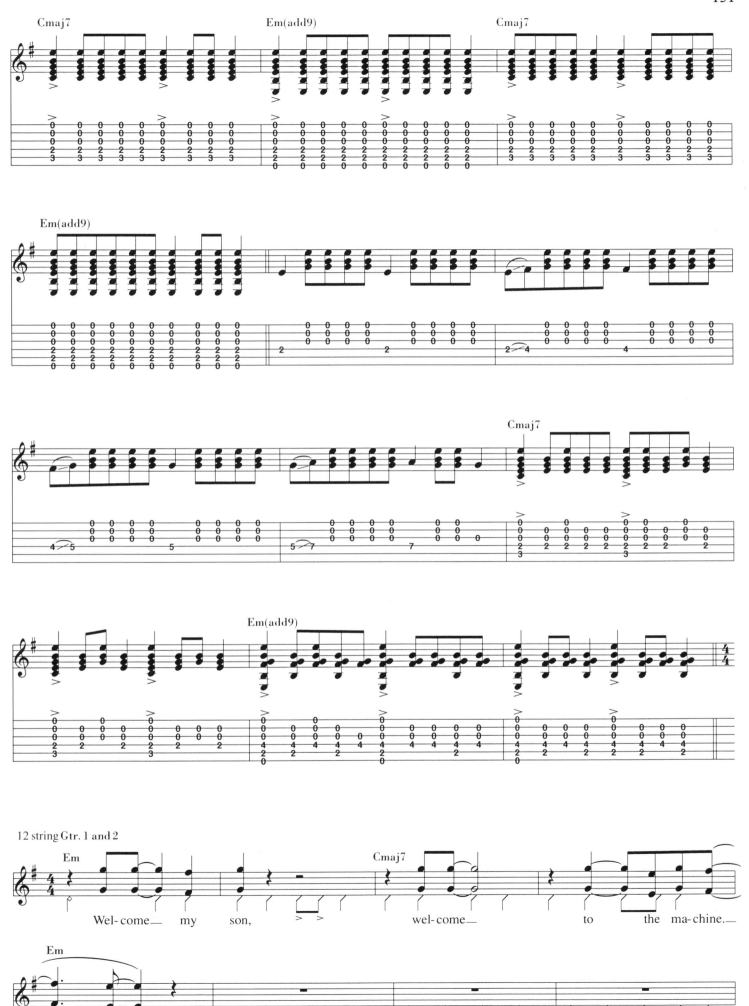

Wel-come— my son, wel-come— to the ma-chine.—